To Alan Shiffrin, MD —

Physician, Colleague, Friend,

& Hope Carrier

Beyond Bipolar

7 Steps to Wellness

Jane Mountain MD

Chapter One Press

Beyond Bipolar — 7 Steps to Wellness
by Jane Mountain MD

www.beyondbipolar.com

This book is not meant to substitute for medical care of
people with bipolar disorder, and treatment should not be
based solely on its contents. Nor is it meant to offer legal
advice, which must be obtained from a practicing attorney.

ISBN-13: 978-0-9719270-6-3
ISBN-10: 0-9719270-6-5
LCCN: 2007903149

Chapter One Press

P.O. BOX 300039
Denver, Colorado 80203-0039
Printed in USA

Editing: Claire Ohman, Ph.D.
Printing: United Graphics, Inc., Mattoon, IL
Cover design & page layout: *fortissimodesign*, Denver, CO
Principal typefaces: Adobe Garamond Premier Pro.
Adobe Myriad Pro, & Letraset Papyrus

Contents

Table of Contents

Acknowledgements

P erhaps the best part about writing and publishing a book is the opportunity to thank special people in our lives, whether they contributed directly or in a sustaining capacity toward the project.

My thanks to all who have contributed to this book through their lives and gifts —

Thank you, Chuck Mountain, my spouse, for you have lived so much of this book and you encourage me in every endeavor. With thanks for your artistic talent as a graphic designer to make this book attractive as well as useful.

Thank you, Alice Weiss Doyel, for mentoring me toward a life of self-acceptance and toward a whole business accommodation, without which, I could not succeed in business.

My thanks to the members of Cherry Creek Toastmasters of Denver who have brought laughter, friendship, and healing communication to my life. Your constant encouragement sustains me in every project I take on.

Thanks to the members of the Depression/Bipolar Recovery Group of Midtown Denver, for inspiring me from your life experiences of going *beyond bipolar*.

Thank you, Linda Lange, for taking account of my needs as well as crunching the numbers of my business. A friend in need is a friend indeed. Also, Mt. 25:40.

Thank you, John McManamy for becoming a friend in the process of writing a foreword for this book.

Thank you, Claire Ohman, for your professionalism in editing this book and for the swimming lessons that gave me a balance in my life that allowed me to work with higher energy.

Thanks to those who have read this book in various stages of its evolution and gave honest feedback: Deborah Amesbury, Janet Ross, Robin Rothman, Morgan and Marilyn Tamsky. Some of you won't recognize that this is the same book you read, but your suggestions were taken to heart and resulted in a substantial rewriting.

Perhaps the worst part about writing and publishing a book is that you don't have the opportunity to thank everyone, or that your memory is deficient enough to neglect to thank those who have contributed the most. Never mind, there will be more books to follow with additional thanking opportunities.

Foreword

This book is about being smart about resiliency.

T HE BOOK YOU ARE READING, *Beyond Bipolar — 7 Steps to Wellness*, is all about a family reunion with your own identity — about regarding and appreciating yourself for who you are rather than your illness.

A few years ago, I came across an Australian study that was different from the thousands I have seen over recent years. It was so astounding that I devoted a special issue of my email newsletter to its findings. An Australian researcher, Sarah Russell PhD, actually asked patients with bipolar disorder what they did to successfully manage their illness.

This kind of knowledge — from people living well with bipolar disorder — is what my friend Jane Mountain refers to as Street Knowledge. In my interactions with my bipolar community, I urge them to become experts in this kind of Street Knowledge. Getting well and staying well involves taking charge of our own recovery. No other expert knows us personally better than we do — but that is not good enough.

Our illness feeds on our fear and ignorance. It takes no prisoners. The antidote to fear and ignorance is being smart and having the courage to be smart.

Smart about medications, smart about our diagnosis, smart about our behaviors, smart about our lifestyles, smart about our support networks, smart about dealing with stress, smart about knowing our strengths and limitations, smart about our spirituality, smart about mindfulness. Smart about being smart.

This is where *Beyond Bipolar — 7 Steps to Wellness* comes in. In a nutshell, the book is about being smart about resiliency. Yes, we may be a vulnerable population, but we're not entirely helpless, either. We can use our resiliency to avoid depression and mania, and to manage our way through the depressions and manias we can't avoid. We can even use our resiliency to aim for and to achieve a life *beyond bipolar*.

Jane Mountain is a medical doctor who knows the value of treatment. She is a patient who has the Street Knowledge to live beyond her illness. Such is the power of being smart about resiliency. In *Beyond Bipolar — 7 Steps to Wellness*, she teaches us about getting our lives back, about daring to hope, and about realizing that hope.

Be hopeful. You have the best person in the world working on your recovery. That person is you.

John McManamy

— Author, *Living Well with Depression and Bipolar Disorder: What Your Doctor Doesn't Tell You...That You Need to Know*

— Editor and Publisher, *McMan's Depression and Bipolar Report, McMan's Depression and Bipolar Web*

Introduction

Introduction

*Recovery is the process of seeking mental wellness
in the context of experiencing bipolar disorder.*

MANY WHO EXPERIENCE BIPOLAR DISORDER have gone before you in their search for recovery. Thankfully, they've discovered that achieving mental wellness is possible, in spite of daunting challenges.

Many, including myself, have been extremely ill, feeling suicidal and hopeless. Some have experienced devastating consequences of mania. Others have had significant pieces of their lives nearly destroyed by divorce, job loss, financial ruin or attempted suicide. Nearly all of us have lost significant relationships along the way. But none of this disqualifies us from seeking recovery. If you experience bipolar disorder — even if you're going through the worst time in your life — you are a candidate for the recovery process. With bipolar disorder, you can never be too sick to recover.

The chief ingredient of recovery is resiliency. Resiliency allows us to spring back or recover from challenges. Resiliency is not something you're born with. Resiliency is a skill set that can be practiced and learned. This is good news, since with bipolar disorder, challenges abound. Seeking mental wellness can be difficult but not impossible. Mental wellness happens! But not without gaining knowledge and skills to manage the curve balls thrown our way. Are you ready to hit that curve ball out of the park?

This book will get you started. Be kind to yourself as you seek recovery. At first you may not see the progress you long for. Have patience with yourself. Expect good things to happen, and allow them to unfold as you learn to apply the resiliency principles in this book. You can read it straight through like any book, but the chapters each cover a topic and may be returned to again and again. Because later principles build on earlier principles described, I suggest you either read straight through the book to get started or take the chapters in order. Once you have done that, return to the principles you choose to work on during a specific time frame.

Perhaps you have already read my book, *Bipolar Disorder — Insights for Recovery*. It contains the basics of bipolar disorder, including expertise from two perspectives: my personal experience of bipolar disorder and my experience as a physician. You may want to start with bipolar disorder before delving into this book because it lays the foundation for this book.

You may already have advanced knowledge about bipolar disorder or perhaps you are new to the subject. Either way, both books help you look at things from a recovery perspective that emphasizes resiliency — a perspective that will stretch your knowledge and expand your mental health horizons.

How Resiliency Principles Relate to Treatment

Resiliency principles do not stand alone in facing the challenges of bipolar disorder. Sometimes a person will hear about recovery or resiliency and think they can use them in place of medication or psychotherapy. If you have bipolar disorder, I can only advise you to continue taking your prescribed medications, and to continue attending psychotherapy sessions.

Resiliency principles are an addition to appropriate treatment with medicines and psychotherapy. They are a part of education about bipolar disorder. Resiliency principles give you additional resources, as an adjunct to treatment, to live well with the challenges of bipolar disorder. They help you use your treatment more effectively, but resiliency principles are not a substitute for treatment.

Bipolar disorder is currently a life-long illness and treatment should be life-long too. Nothing I say in this book is meant to encourage you to stop your treatment. If you think it is reasonable to stop your medications, my advice is to remain in treatment and only make any medication changes with the help of your doctor. If you are not currently in treatment, I encourage you to seek treatment. If you are having difficulties with the medications you are on, I recommend you talk to your prescriber to work out a better plan together.

STREET KNOWLEDGE

This book is not about medical treatment with medications, nor is it about psychotherapy. It is about the principles of resiliency that others with bipolar disorder have discovered. Some of these principles come from various forms of psychotherapy. Most, however, are what I call "Street Knowledge" about bipolar disorder. Much of this book is flavored by my life-long attendance in the school of hard-knocks and the Street Knowledge that comes from living with bipolar disorder on a day-by-day basis.

The Street Knowledge I have captured in this book has many

sources. Working in peer relationships with hundreds of people with bipolar disorder and their family members, in addition to participating in the mental health recovery movement has unearthed the day-to-day Street Knowledge that I bring you in this book. I've also grabbed Street Knowledge from proven psychotherapy and recovery sources, but have taken it out of its original form and morphed it into a practical resource that you can put to good use.

Resiliency principles are about you and your desire for mental wellness. They are about focusing on the positive aspects of living with bipolar disorder and managing the challenges. As you are on the road to recovery, use these proven tools that lead toward mental wellness. Treatment is a must for your plan, even though it is not the subject of this book. Street Knowledge of bipolar disorder will add an additional dimension because its roots are in the actual experience of the illness, not just a medical description of the disorder.

Make the recovery process work for you by using all your resources. In this book I want to introduce you to resiliency principles as well as reinforce your understanding of them. In applying these principles, you will learn to manage bipolar disorder to better achieve your goal of mental wellness.

BEYOND BIPOLAR

In my work as a speaker, author and mental health advocate, I meet hundreds of people who are facing and overcoming the challenges of bipolar disorder. They do so by tapping into every helpful resource available to them from medical treatments to resiliency principles, and through support or recovery groups to community services. A consistent focus on wellness and problem solving enables them to live and grow through the illness experience to go *beyond bipolar* in search of mental wellness.

No matter how sick you may be, or how gifted or how stable on medications, there is always more to learn about going *beyond bipolar* to a life of mental wellness. I have presented these principles to people of all walks of life and the feedback I receive is that they can be life changing! Most are teased from proven (evidence-based) practices, and I have put them into the every day language of experience for easier access.

In going *beyond bipolar*, we can make better use of the gifts that often accompany bipolar disorder. High intelligence, enhanced creativity and unique insights far outshine the negative associations that can accompany the diagnosis of a lifelong psychiatric disorder. In going *beyond bipolar*, we can achieve a greater mood stability that empowers us to use our creative talents.

Others of us feel as though we have missed out on the "creative gifts" of bipolar disorder. Especially if we became ill at an early age or if we have been extremely ill, we may not have discovered the romanticized creativity that is supposed to accompany this illness. Retaining or regaining our creativity may not be an issue for us. We just want to have our lives back! Resiliency principles will help in this challenge, and along the way we may discover strengths we didn't know we had.

Three Requirements for Mental Wellness

There are three requirements that can help us experience mental wellness in spite of having symptoms of bipolar disorder. First, learn all you can about the diagnosis and treatment of bipolar disorder. That is, learn so much about bipolar disorder that you become an expert. My first book, *Bipolar Disorder — Insights for Recovery,* covered this requirement in some depth, and even more resources are found on my website at www.BeyondBipolar.com.

Becoming an expert enables you to seek the appropriate services from your doctors and clinicians.

Second, understand the lessons of resiliency — the topic of this book. Resiliency helps you manage bipolar disorder instead of letting it manage you. It helps you develop a lifelong recovery plan. In fact, these lessons are the foundation that allows you to live with bipolar disorder every day — not just from appointment to appointment.

Third, develop recovery skills to apply in your daily life. You'll depend on these skills when you're having challenges as well as when you're feeling well. Bipolar disorder is nearly always a lifelong condition that may have remissions and recurrences. Because of this, recovery skills are best used daily, no matter how you feel. This book guides you through those skills.

Lessons of resiliency lay the groundwork for learning and applying recovery skills. Suggested recovery skills are peppered throughout this book because they fit hand in glove with resiliency lessons. By understanding resiliency, you also get the knack of adding recovery skills that you develop yourself.

Be kind to yourself as you work with the principles in this book. Seeking mental wellness is a process that takes time. Applying these principles and skills has helped people like you and me achieve a fulfilling level of personal mental health. But this doesn't happen overnight or without hard work. Your starting point will be hope. Chapter 1 will help you find some. You will have times of frustration and discouragement, and times of improvement and joy — perhaps more of the former at first. You have this disorder, so why not fight it with all the strength you have?

Your goal? Become resilient!

Step 1

Hope!

Hope is the essential ingredient in the recovery process.

I N MY STUDY OF RECOVERY from bipolar disorder and my own personal search for mental wellness, I've found that hope plays a key role. In fact, I can't remember ever making progress toward mental wellness without hope. There have been times when I was not the person with hope; I often had to rely on another's hope.

Finding hope can be challenging. My lack of hope often kept me from going *beyond bipolar* toward mental wellness. Then I learned to search for hope whenever my sense of hope was fading. Searching for hope is a recovery skill deriving from the principle that *hope is the essential ingredient in the recovery process.*

FINDING HOPE

Sometimes hope is the most difficult ingredient to find, especially when things are going badly. It can be difficult or seem impossible to focus on hope when we're feeling discouraged or depressed. But have you ever thought about searching for hope?

1

Mania can have the opposite impact, filling us with hope that may not be based in reality. Mania's spin on hope may be too cheery, causing added disappointments when mania gives way to depression.

With bipolar disorder, we experience times in our lives when we can't grasp hope. During these times, we must let others carry our hope in order to go on living — to "catch" hope just as we would catch a cold. Catching a cold isn't difficult; all it takes is being around people who have colds. The same is true of hope. Let's get exposed to hope and let it infect us! Here are some ways to do this.

The Ingredient of Hope

Once I experienced severe, life-threatening depression over a period of many months. I lost hope. I was a veteran at seeking treatment and I habitually stayed on medications as prescribed. Kudos for me! I was the ideal patient. The frustration of lagging progress was daunting. My experience was that of many whose medical treatment doesn't kick in before multiple trials of medications. Psychotherapy played an important role, but the depression was brutal, leaving me devoid of hope.

At this point in my life with bipolar disorder, the word recovery would easily dispirit me because it seemed so difficult to achieve. I feared it was out of my grasp forever. I yearned intensely to get better, but my efforts seemed to fall flat. I was missing the essential ingredient: hope.

While feeling this way, I attended a conference focused on hope. An eloquent presenter told how she'd found hope after being hospitalized for 15 years with a psychiatric diagnosis. During her recovery, she attended graduate school and was now working full time. Talk about hope! That's exactly what she did — for three hours straight. She oozed hope, with riveting statements like these:

- We should have hope because others have found recovery.
- Hope is necessary and real because we are always growing in our ability to learn to live with psychiatric disorders.
- Examples of hope include the achievements of those who have been challenged by bipolar disorder.
- Hope is real because treatment is improving all the time.
- We cannot forget hope because there are those in this world who love and need us.
- Hope can be found in the midst of discouragement, and this is an experience well documented by historical accounts.

The courage and strength of character of those living with psychiatric disorders flavored the true stories she shared. And hope was the main ingredient in each person's life as recovery was sought and achieved.

I call people like this speaker "hope carriers." Her message of hope fed me, because I was famished and it nourished me with the main ingredient I needed to succeed in recovery. I didn't come away from the presentation gushing with hope; rather, I had tasted hope and saw that it was satisfying.

Hope is the essential ingredient in the recovery process. Some chefs will search throughout the world for an essential ingredient, but in my life the essential ingredient of hope had been missing because I hadn't been seeking it. Instead I was bewailing my life in deep despair and not smelling or tasting hope even when it was beneath my very nose.

PICTURES OF HOPE

By visualizing hope, we are more likely to recognize it in our own lives. A memory from my childhood paints a picture that illustrates this. When my family used to visit my Grandma, we passed near a huge factory whose sole product seemed to be an overwhelming stench.

But worse than that was the sight of miles and miles of workers' homes provided by the corporation that owned the factory. Miles and miles of hopeless shack houses centered upon a belching factory. Tiny shack homes, unpainted, with postage stamp yards of bare dirt. They were obviously inhabited but without curtains or even a single distinguishing characteristic. They are all alike in their poverty of spirit — all but one that I eagerly watch for.

Ah, there it is, its colorful painted sides, its white picket fence and green grass contrasting sharply with the shacks around it. The curtains and painted walls shout hope in the hopeless, drab and desolate community.

Hope looks like this house. It contrasts with all around it.

Hope believes the music of your life can become more harmonious. No matter how out of tune things get, the music of your life can become more harmonious. It doesn't matter how long you've been struggling to find hope. Recovery studies show that the darkest time in the course of an illness frequently triggers permanent change through taking steps to recovery. Things do change, and often for the better! Create in your mind pictures of what hope might look like so you recognize it when you see it.

NURTURING HOPE

With the ingredient of hope, things don't have to be perfect before we can make progress toward recovery. In fact, hope puts adversity in perspective and improves our resilience. By reminding ourselves of our strengths, we can put our challenges into perspective. We all know bipolar disorder is a challenging illness, but when we remember to nurture hope, we actually get better.

Looking back, it's easy to see we could have made wiser decisions, treated someone better or done things differently. It's possible we may even need to ask for forgiveness from others. We have the power to take responsibility for unacceptable behavior during our extremes of mania, and we don't have to beat ourselves up for activities we couldn't accomplish during times of depression.

After all, we don't choose to have bipolar disorder. It helps us to realize that no matter how bizarre and non-productive our activities may have been, we can learn and grow from these experiences. We can emphasize our strengths as well as accept our challenges.

The key is to distinguish between the illness that affects us and the people we are. Sometimes, the illness simply overwhelms us. Support from others may not have been available or adequate. We thought we were doing well on our own but we became very ill without realizing it. We didn't know we needed treatment. Despite this, a healthy person is waiting to appear or reappear in each of us. We are far greater than the illness we experience.

The Pie

A friend of mine talks about the pie that represents our life and person. Each of us has many pieces to our pie. Some pieces in my pie include being a spouse and mother — even a mother-in-law! Other pieces are being a Lutheran Christian, retired physician, musician, speaker, friend, and author. Similarly, when we live with bipolar disorder, one piece of our pie represents our health.

In other words, bipolar disorder is something that requires our ongoing attention to feel good.

Although I prefer to have the bipolar piece remain a tiny sliver, at times when I was very ill, bipolar disorder filled most of the pie. When it's just a sliver, the other parts of my life are freer to flourish. But it's still a piece of the pie because I need to pay enough attention to it in order to be healthy in spite of its challenges.

Because you're reading this book, it's clear you're looking for the missing ingredients in your pie of life. Persistently seek the help you need until you find it. You can revive the parts of yourself that have been lost in the experience of illness. Bake a pie with dough swollen by hope so every piece of you life can achieve consistency and sweetness. *Hope is the essential ingredient in the recovery process*

FINDING HOPE

Beg, borrow, or steal hope wherever you can get it! Sniff it out like a hound dog. Search for people who express hope. Spend time with them catching the fever of hope. *Hope is the essential ingredient in the recovery process.*

When I was experiencing my worst depression, I turned to several people who carried my hope for me. One was my psychiatrist. Echoing with despair, I would ask him if I would ever get better. With great optimism, he would always say "Yes, definitely." Frankly, his zealous response led me to believe he was the one needing psychiatric care, not me. Still, no matter how we react to hope carriers, we need them to help us through times of famine.

Another hope carrier for me is my Aunt Donna. She catches the scent of my despair and takes me out for a lunch of nutritious food featuring the main course of hope.

Speaking the Language of Hope

Here are some ways to express hope for the future:
- When I am better…(not *if I get better*).
- I look forward to…(not *I dread*).
- When I can…(not *if I can*).
- I wish I could…(not *I should*).
- I hope that…(not *I fear that*).

Hope doesn't always belong in the future. Try these out for the present:
- Now that I'm on the path to getting better…
- I am proud of myself for reading this book.
- By reading this book, I have taken my first step toward recovery.
- Today is a new chance to begin again.
- I can do things differently.
- Change for me can begin today.

In hope statements, don't forget the past either. Many of us carry a burden of guilt because of the way we look at the past. Try these on for size:
- I did the best I could during a difficult time…(not *I really failed at…*)
- I wish I had…(not *I should have*)
- Yesterday was a challenge… (not *yesterday was a disaster*)
- I tried my best…(not *if only I had or hadn't done…*)

Don't be dispirited if hope remains tantalizingly out of reach for a while. Hopelessness can be a part of the experience of bipolar disorder, which I have also experienced. Although hopelessness may feel never-ending, it is not: In my work I have seen hundreds of people with bipolar disorder discover or regain hope. You can too! Get hungry enough to forage for hope until you find it.

BORROWING HOPE

Until you find hope, borrow from others just as you would borrow a cup of sugar from a neighbor. Seek the company of individuals and organizations that consistently express hope. Community and mental health organizations can sometimes be great places from which to borrow hope. Some hopeful people will be hanging out at your workplace, in your neighborhood or other places you go every day. Personally, I find hopeful people in my Toastmasters group and in the Depression/Bipolar Recovery Group of Midtown Denver.

Many find hopeful people in volunteer positions. Libraries, hospitals, mental health associations, faith groups, book clubs, botanic gardens, musical groups and animal shelters — all are places to find people from whom to borrow hope.

Here are some examples of how I borrow hope from others. I spend time around hopeful people and observe what they do. I listen for hope statements and try them on for size. For example, I remember the first time I identified the words, "I am confidant that I can succeed."

The phrase, "I am confident" is foreign to my usual way of thinking. I am more likely to say, "I'm not sure this will work", or "I think this might work", or even "I am fearful". "I am confident" is a hope phrase. I borrowed it from a hopeful person. Now I use it all the time. It has become like a borrowed book in my library, whose original owner I no longer remember. Borrow hope! *Hope is the essential ingredient in the recovery process.*

EXPRESSING HOPE

Hope is the key ingredient in the recovery process. Let's talk about this essential ingredient using hopeful words. It may be difficult to express hope when your heart isn't truly in it. Do it anyway. It's okay to practice saying words of hope in front of a mirror, while exercising or in the shower. Each time you say them, affirm them with more energy. Do you think this is phony or silly? It may feel this way, but expressing hope is always appropriate as long as it acknowledges and validates that challenges are real.

Hope would have no meaning without suffering. Within this context, hope finds its greatest expression. Hope doesn't ignore the reality of challenges and the tremendous pain of an illness that takes over your life at times. Suffering doesn't preclude hope — it engenders hope.

Know that it's okay to express hope in desperate situations, and it's okay to talk about hope in your daily activities. In your self-talk, declare that you look forward to a time when you will feel better. Affirm hope by reading quotations, by being around hopeful people, and by making statements of hope. Go ahead — express hope.

FINDING OURSELVES

Hope helps us bake our pies in the midst of the challenges of bipolar disorder. We cannot be passive about hope, for our very lives depend on finding hope. Search for its ingredients. Make it a practice to beg, borrow, or steal hope wherever you can find it! *Hope is the essential ingredient of the recovery process.* When in doubt, hope! When discouraged, hope!

On the next two pages are some exercises to help you find hope. Try to use them every day so they become familiar:

A. Try these statements on for size. Say them while you are alone and then try them out when talking to others. If you like, add your own in the spaces provided, or on your mirror or refrigerator.

- I am confident that I will get better.

- I will find the help that I need.

- Others have learned to live with bipolar disorder, and I will too.

- My life is tough now, but I have the courage to deal with this.

- I am confident that I can manage through the good and the bad.

- _____

- _____

- _____

B. Ask yourself these questions and take action to make a plan.

- Who do I know that expresses hope about my illness? Am I spending enough time with that person?

- Is there anyone in my life who is discouraging me from being mentally well? Am I spending too much time with that person without the balance of others who encourage me?

- Would it be helpful if I could find a community group, perhaps a support or recovery group, which would help me be around hopeful people?

- Write three things you can do to find more hope in your life:

    1. _____

    2. _____

    3. _____

C. Here are ways I can beg, borrow or steal hope when I am discouraged:

    - Keep a list of hopeful quotations and read them each morning and evening.

    - Call a supportive friend or family member and talk for five or ten minutes.

    - _____

    - _____

    - _____

Beyond Bipolar — 7 Steps to Wellness

Step 2
Manage!

Management drives resiliency.

EVERYONE'S LIFE IS FULL OF CHALLENGES. For those of us with bipolar disorder, even ordinary challenges can become complicated, because bipolar disorder can unexpectedly throw us off balance from the normal flow of life. Episodes can be small or can take titanic bites from our lives. They can overwhelm not only us, but our family and friends as well. When overwhelmed we often cope rather than manage. *Management drives resiliency.*

THE DIFFERENCE BETWEEN MANAGING AND COPING

The verb "to cope" has its root in words that mean to slash, to deal with and attempt to overcome problems and difficulties. Coping carries us through difficult times, especially if we have learned skillful tactics to approach problems. However, when bipolar disorder has us in its grip, fluctuating moods can leave us fragile and undermine our ability to cope.

Sometimes we cope by working or playing harder, sometimes by debating with ourselves whether or not we want to live. But all too often we hack away without really weighing the results. It is better that we slash wildly (cope) at our challenges rather than ignore them or passively give in to them. In our fierce slashing we sometimes forget to ask questions like these:

- What actually works?

- What works when bipolar disorder isn't complicating things?

- What doesn't work at all?

- What has worked in the past?

Next consider the root of the word manage. Manage comes from a Latin word meaning "hand", as in handling a horse: to put it through its paces, to direct it with a degree of skill, to guide its tremendous power and potential into something useful and beautiful. An alternative to stormy coping is to go *beyond bipolar* by learning to manage its power and potential. This is important because our goal is not just existing through bipolar disorder but achieving mental wellness. In the long run, our dealings with bipolar disorder need to focus on learning to manage. *Management drives resiliency.*

COPING LEAVES US STUCK

The process of moving from coping to managing is a vital step in learning resiliency in the face of bipolar disorder. It can take us from being very ill to being able to live a resilient life in spite of having a recurrent challenge. With patience we can hone our skills as we learn to manage bipolar disorder.

Sometimes misdirected coping skills (slashing) are enough to get us through immediate challenges. But they don't always work well in the long term. Coping without managing can lead us to a place where we feel stuck, unable to step back or go forward. Clearly, using management skills works better than coping and helps us have more success facing the challenges of bipolar disorder. *Management drives resiliency.*

Here's an example in which coping got me through a difficult time yet, in the end, left me stuck. At one of the worst times in my illness, I was suicidal. I wasn't just thinking about suicide — I was planning. Soon my plans were complete and I was just waiting for the right opportunity. My plans included having to walk a distance in the dark. One part of me didn't want to carry out my plans and that part kept reminding me that since childhood I had been afraid of the dark. But most of me longed to be out of my misery. Still there was a small, buried part that hoped I would feel better some day.

Whenever I felt like acting on my plans, I coped by recalling my fear of the dark. I convinced myself that I couldn't act because my plan required me to endure the dreaded darkness. My plan did not include management skills, and it didn't help me recover from this threat to my life.

This rather ineffective coping kept me alive, but it might not have. At any point, my desire to be rid of the intense pain may have become stronger than my fear of the dark, and I even thought of changing my plan to remove the requirement of darkness from the scheme. Although this method of coping helped keep me alive, it didn't allow me the resiliency to put suicidal thoughts behind me and make progress toward recovery.

Manage!

Then I began to manage instead of cope. I decided not to act on suicidal urges. I put a note in my wallet that said, "I need help. I feel suicidal." I showed the note to a few trusted friends, and I taught them what to do if ever I showed them the note. I resolved to call a friend when I needed support. When suicidal thoughts came, I told those thoughts, "No! Go away! Get out of my head — leave my thinking alone!" Finally, I considered a short hospital stay to give me a break from the strong suicidal urges. Although I didn't have to use this latter plan, it helped to see it as an option.

Adding management skills to treatment takes you *beyond bipolar* and to a new place. When you move *beyond bipolar* you can draw from your positive attributes rather than bogging down in the challenges of this illness. *Management drives resiliency.*

Management is a process that occurs in several stages. When we manage something, we first learn as much as we can about it. Then we identify goals and challenges to reaching those goals. Next we propose plans and solutions. We then chose a plan and try it out. Finally we evaluate the effectiveness of our plan and tweak it to make it better — or change to a new plan that has greater possibilities. Sometimes we need to retrace our steps, perhaps to choose a more appropriate goal, or to continue learning.

We know this process of problem solving from other parts of our lives. We may be expert at solving math problems, doing crossword puzzles or balancing our checkbooks. For others, planning a garden seems effortless. As we do these activities, we hardly realize that we are following a management procedure. But the strong moods of bipolar disorder may kidnap us to a place where problem solving is thrown out the window. Moods may be so strong we think we have to act on them unquestioningly instead of stopping to identify problems and solve them.

Some of us may not be experienced with following a problem solving process. Or perhaps our process lacks a crucial step. Perhaps we educate ourselves well about a challenge and set goals easily but then fail to follow through. Or we are in the middle of our plan but doggedly slash forward without evaluating if our plan accomplishes our goals. *Management drives resiliency.*

Managers learn the steps of problem solving and use them regularly. This can be applied to the challenges of bipolar disorder, and with practice, can take us forward in recovery. Here are the steps again:

1. Identify one or two goals and the challenges you will have in reaching them. (Perhaps your first goal will be to finish this book!)

2. Propose possible plans to meet your goal or goals.

3. Choose a plan and try it out.

4. Evaluate the effectiveness of your plan. If it isn't working well, ask yourself whether you need to give it more time, or to go back to one of the earlier steps in the process to try a different plan.

Medical Description vs. Illness Experience

The medical description of a disorder and its illness experience are two different things. To medically describe a disorder, experts refer to the sciences of anatomy, physiology, pathology, psychiatry, psychology, nutrition and other disciplines. An illness experience differs from a medical description because it varies from person to person. It's how we experience the disorder, not how we describe its symptoms.

For example, if I have diabetes, I may experience it quite differently from another person with diabetes. I may see diabetes as a challenge that requires me to exercise, watch my diet and take good care of myself. Or I may see diabetes as something to be ashamed of. I may start out sicker than others at the time of diagnosis. My family may be supportive of my challenges — or not know how to support me.

Some people who face cultural issues may have to make bigger changes when adapting recipes than someone who already eats a diabetes-friendly diet. Perhaps a close relative has diabetes too, and I see how sick diabetes can sometimes make a person. This could cause me to fear having diabetes. Fear could either make me give up trying to be healthy, or motivate me to work harder to take care of myself.

So, while the science of medicine describes diabetes the same for everyone who has a type of diabetes, the art of medicine recognizes that the illness experience can be different for each of us.

The focus of recovery with bipolar disorder is not the medical description of the disorder. Rather, it is effectively aimed at the illness experience, or the place where bipolar disorder touches your daily life. How you experience bipolar disorder will determine which management skills will help you most. I call the knowledge you need to deal with the illness experience Street Knowledge.

Of course, understanding and applying medical knowledge plays a major role in managing your disease using medications and therapy. However, if you only focus on diagnosis and medication, you may fail to deal with the illness experience. This is the main place where you can make changes to improve your mental wellness. Learn as much as possible about Street Knowledge which helps you in daily living.

PATIENCE TO TAME THE HORSE

Managing is vital to resiliency. Always be patient with yourself, especially while you are learning. You may have managed your life successfully at another time in your life, but bipolar disorder is a different horse. Even if the horse has been in control for years, you can learn to use the reins to advance to a point where you can manage its challenges.

Here are some things to think about in learning to manage:

1. Has bipolar disorder consumed the entire pie of your life?

2. Do you see yourself as "being bipolar" or as having bipolar disorder? Perhaps you might try having this illness, instead of being it. (If you had cancer you would not say, "I'm cancer.")

3. Can you try taking a challenge related to your illness that is important to you? For example, make a new friend, attend a support or recovery group for the first time, find a job, achieve a promotion, go to school, or get out of bed each morning. Now come up with a plan to reach your goal through problem solving.

4. Are you afraid to ride the horse of bipolar disorder? Is it easier to ignore it? Would applying management skills help tame the horse?

5. Are you normally a "take charge" type of person? Is it frustrating that you haven't been able to take charge of bipolar disorder? Could you be coping instead of managing? If so, how can you change this picture?

6. Are you getting hopeful input from others? Your friends, your family, your doctor, your therapist, your pastor, your mentor, your peers? Or are you trying to manage bipolar disorder on your own?

7. Where are you getting the Street Knowledge you need? Have you made other friends who have bipolar disorder?

Can you join a support or recovery group? Can you get quality Street Knowledge through books and on the Internet?

8. Are you are always with others who have bipolar disorder and are missing input from friendships whose primary focus is not your shared illness experience?

Step 3

Aim!

Resiliency is the target for achieving mental wellness.

SEEKING MENTAL WELLNESS within the experience of bipolar disorder can be like playing darts. Although you score more the closer your dart lands to the bull's eye in the center of the target, you don't always have to hit the bull's eye. For a beginner, just being able to hit any area of the target is an initial goal. Scoring a bull's eye comes later with practice and it still doesn't happen with every throw.

In this case the whole target is resiliency, not just the bull's eye of normal mood. To achieve mental wellness, we don't need to worry about hitting the bull's eye all the time, but rather hitting anywhere on the target of resiliency. Too often we shoot for perfection, or normal mood.

There are two problems with this.

First, those of us who experience bipolar disorder rarely know what normal mood is — we can't see the bull's eye! Second, it's impossible to hit a bull's eye every time we throw the dart. Achieving the target of mental wellness means being functional in as many essential areas of our lives as possible. Below I've quoted the former Surgeon General's definition of mental wellness in his report on mental health in America. Notice that it emphasizes functioning in vital areas of life.

> Mental health refers to the successful performance of mental function, resulting in productive activities, fulfilling relationships with other people, and the ability to adapt to change and cope with adversity. (*Mental Health: A Report of the Surgeon General*, 1999, p. 4.)

In other words, mental wellness doesn't exclude having an illness in our lives, whether it's psychiatric or not. Nor does it exclude facing challenges. People can gain mental wellness *beyond bipolar* and deal with life's everyday challenges by hitting the target of resiliency.

To establish a baseline for recovery, first we define our target and the bull's eye. The bull's eye is normal mood. But what is normal mood? By recognizing normal mood you can see it as a bull's eye. No matter that you may aim for a bull's eye, your goal remains to hit the target of resiliency. When you hit this target, you are functioning successfully enough to score in some way, even though you aren't hitting the bull's eye of normal mood all the time.

Normal mood is a baseline — a bull's eye — for resiliency and should be a guide to managing your overall mood. Normal mood is characterized by resiliency, an ability to bounce back within a normal range. Understanding normal mood helps us understand the world we live in. Indeed, those of us who experience bipolar disorder find normal mood difficult to recognize. We have the psychiatric ability to experience a much wider range of mood than most people. Our range includes not just the bull's eye and the target — it includes the entire wall, perhaps the entire room where the target is located.

This wider range can both empower and impoverish us. The empowerment of bipolar disorder can lead to highly creative, purpose-driven activities that potentially may enrich others as well as ourselves. Those of us with bipolar disorder see things differently, enabling us to create unique solutions to all kinds of challenges. This special way of seeing may be part of what we value most about ourselves. It may be part of the distinct gift we have to offer others.

However, when our range of mood includes the entire room, we can also suffer deeply. Out of control mania can shatter relationships and derail occupational goals. Similarly, depression can be crushing, taking from us the enjoyment of family, friends, job and recreation. It can even lead to self-injury and death. The extremes of mania and depression can impoverish our lives.

By knowing where the bull's eye of normal mood is, we can better aim for the target of resiliency. Being able to recognize normal mood in others helps us avoid the negative consequences of these extremes. We can recognize normal mood as the center of the target. Aiming for the target of resiliency, which includes both normal mood and the defined space surrounding it, lets us know when our experience of mood misses the target and hits the wall. We may be a bit off the bull's eye of normal mood, but staying in the range of the target rather than hitting the walls can help us function and achieve mental wellness. *Resiliency is the target for achieving mental wellness.*

UNDERSTANDING RESILIENCY AND SET POINT

One characteristic of normal mood is resiliency which is the bouncing back quality that keeps it within a normal range. Resiliency helps a person exist in the zone of normal mood no matter what is happening to push mood outside of normal. It naturally stops the brain from stepping outside of well-regulated mood.

With bipolar disorder, however, we frequently step (more likely, run) far outside of well-regulated mood. That is, our mood soars into mania or plunges into depression. The challenge of bipolar disorder is dealing with the brain's inability to consistently regulate mood within a normal range. In other words, instead of hitting the bull's eye, we hit the walls.

Gaining resiliency helps those of us with bipolar disorder bounce back to a functional mood, the mood that hits the target, if not the bull's eye. Resiliency is one of the primary characteristics of normal mood, and it's also a characteristic that we need to develop if we want to hit the target of mental wellness.

For those who experience normal mood, it is as though there is a "set point" that helps keep a person's mood stable within a comfortable range, much like a thermostat works to keep the temperature of one's house within a comfortable range. When mood begins to move too far in one direction, the brain sees movement away from the set point and resiliency reins it back into the zone of normal mood.

For people with bipolar disorder, a set point for normal mood doesn't seem to exist much of the time. A brain that doesn't recognize the set point automatically won't kick in the resiliency to keep mood within a normal range. Instead, the mood regulator gets stuck at a higher or lower level. Sometimes the brain gets into a cycle of swinging back and forth between extremes, always missing the set point. This rapid cycling takes the person from mania to depression and back again, sometimes within days or even minutes.

Sometimes the brain may aim at the set point — but end up on both sides of it at once! In this case, you might experience both the energy of mania and hopelessness of depression at the same time. This could indicate a mixed mood. At times, I have experienced characteristics of mixed mood. I have the energy to do the things I want to, but I also may burst into tears without expecting to. Many people who have heard me share this concept have said that understanding the concept of mixed mood was a powerful insight in learning to live with bipolar disorder.

In contrast to the extremes of mood, resiliency keeps mood from monopolizing our thought lives and actions. It allows feeling sad over a loss but still being able to have an enjoyable time with friends. It allows bouncing back with problem solving when difficulties arise. You can be happy about the positive things of life without ignoring its challenges. To go *beyond bipolar*, we must recognize a set point for normal mood at some level, and this set point becomes the bull's eye that helps us identify the target. *Resiliency is the target for achieving mental wellness.*

MAKING IT EASY

Resiliency is the ability to bounce back. If resiliency is our target, we want to stay focused on resiliency in seeking mental wellness. The more you know about the target, the easier it is to hit. It includes hitting the target most of the time. If we miss the target of resiliency, we can correct our next throw of the dart by asking ourselves what we need to do differently. But if we don't know what resiliency looks like, we will have a tough time correcting our next throw.

Just as the game of darts can be learned through practice, the real-life game of resiliency can be learned with practice. The first step is to begin noticing resiliency in our lives and the lives of others. Did you notice the shift of taking our sight off of our experience of illness in order to find another target — resiliency — that will give us new goals?

At first our attempts will be off target. Occasionally we will hit the target almost by accident. Eventually our attempts will take us closer to the target and then to the bull's eye, or normal mood. Your medications may help you hit the bull's eye of normal mood right away, but it is still important to practice for the times when things get off target. When medications take longer to work for you or you haven't yet found a good combination, practice is also essential.

Target practice helps us identify and aim for the target of resiliency. If we develop resiliency of mood, we won't be overtaken by the whims of bipolar disorder. We know that we'll hit the target more frequently as time goes on. Remember, recovery is a process. A process takes time, but it also requires that we have a target so we can improve our aim. To go *beyond bipolar* to mental wellness, we must take aim. *Resiliency is the target for achieving mental wellness.*

STAYING IN THE GAME

The time to practice is not in the midst of a dart game. During the game is when we apply the skills we have achieved. Likewise with bipolar disorder, the time to practice is everyday, no matter how we feel. It is during the times when we feel our best that we sometimes accomplish the most to hone our resiliency skills. Then, when we are in the midst of depression, hypomania, mania, or mixed mood, we can pull out our darts and remember what it felt like to aim and throw at the target of resiliency.

Don't be dispirited if you feel as though you are always in the game and never get a practice break. If this is currently your experience of bipolar disorder, consider the game a practice session. Gradually you will get closer to the target as long as you don't give up. Although you may frequently feel like giving up, giving up is the only thing that can keep you from becoming resilient.

Giving up is not an option. You are in the game for life, and your life depends on it. You may need a time out such as a short hospitalization, a ten-minute break to scream your frustration, a five-minute walk around the block, or a brief talk with a friend. Keep your time outs short, and get back to the game as soon as possible.

Keep on target by practicing as much as possible. Keep aiming no matter what your skill level. Go *beyond bipolar* by seeking mental wellness. *Resiliency is the target for achieving mental wellness.* Keep throwing those darts! Here are some questions to help you find or define the target:

1. Does normal mood seem like a strange concept to you? Have you ever had a time when you thought you were experiencing normal mood? What did that feel like? What were you able to accomplish during that time?

2. Have you been shooting for a tiny bull's eye instead of recognizing your progress in hitting the target around the bull's eye? Do you believe you could take some of the stress off your goal by seeking a resilient mood rather than a normal mood? Could that resilient mood be close enough to normal mood to help you become more functional?

3. Do you ever take time outs from your illness? How do you do this? When you do, can you see these as a healthy

response to your illness rather than as a failure? Can you use your time outs to help you get back into the game for the long haul? Could a time out help you boost your desire to continue in the game?

4. Have you ever wanted to quit the game altogether by giving up on treatment or by taking your life? Are you able to look instead to a future in which you will feel better? Do you need to get help sooner when these thoughts arise? Have you shared these thoughts with your doctor or therapist?

5. Have you ever imagined yourself having a resilient mood? Is resiliency something you could aim for? Are you resilient in other areas of your life but inflexible when it comes to facing bipolar disorder? Are you actively looking for resiliency resources?

Step 4

Search!

Discovering mood clues is essential
in playing the game of bipolar disorder.

IN PLAYING THE GAME OF BIPOLAR DISORDER, we are nearly always taught to focus on episodes of depression or mania rather than look for subtle mood clues. Mood clues tell us where our mood might be headed at a particular time. Episodes tell us where our moods have arrived.

Mood episodes are medically defined and last for a certain length of time. They include depression, hypomania, mania, and mixed mood. Episodes have a specific number of symptoms that are identified by clinicians to diagnose the overall picture of bipolar disorder.

By focusing on episodes, we are trying to avoid depression or mania. Often we don't react until we have an episode, and by then our reaction is late in the game and we are already behind in the final quarter. This is a defensive position. When our mood is more stable (perhaps in a normal, or close to normal mood), we forget we are even in the game! That's when some people stop all medications and forget that they even have bipolar disorder. We might live with a dread we are losing the game, but we forget that playing the game is important. We go our merry way without continuing to be on the offensive in order to win the game.

Focusing on mood clues gives us an alternative approach to help us go *beyond bipolar* toward mental wellness. Instead of waiting for an episode to come along before reacting, we can be working toward mental wellness on a daily basis. Mood clues are subtle when compared to episodes. We can deal with them early in simple ways. Paying attention to them can prevent them growing into episodes. *Discovering mood clues is essential in playing the game of bipolar disorder.*

The episodes of bipolar disorder are described as times when a person with bipolar disorder has a mood (such as depression or mania) that lasts a certain length of time and is characterized by specific symptoms. It takes one week to qualify as an episode of mania and two weeks for depression. (A hospitalization for mania will meet criteria no matter what the time interval.) In most instances, episodes last far longer than one or two weeks. A pre-defined number of specific symptoms needs to be present to diagnose an episode, although not everyone has exactly the same symptoms.

If we are planning to suicide, that is a symptom of depression that we readily recognize. A buying spree that runs us into bankruptcy is a symptom of mania. Both of these are more than mood clues. They are well-defined symptoms. They're often part of full-blown episodes of depression or mania.

However, those of us who experience bipolar disorder see a few mood clues that may not last long enough or be severe enough to qualify as symptoms making up an episode. It makes sense that if the brain has difficulty finding a set point for mood, it may stray from normal mood in small as well as in the large ways that make up an episode.

For example, with bipolar disorder, we might not experience an episode of depression, but we can experience sadness greater than normal in the absence of other features of depression. Or maybe we don't experience mania for an entire week, but instead have a few days of increased energy and racing thoughts. These kinds of mood clues are as important in managing bipolar disorder as the episodes are! They help us go *beyond bipolar* to seek mental wellness.

Later chapters will talk about what to do with mood clues once we discover them, but as a first step, start searching for mood clues. I find it helpful to divide them into mood clues of depression and mania (including hypomania). Each of us, with practice, will identify mood clues that are unique to us as individuals.

You are looking for the first mood clues that indicate that your mood is changing or becoming unstable. The reason you are looking for them is to get a better understanding of where your mood is at any given time. *Discovering mood clues is essential in playing the game of bipolar disorder.*

Recognizing Mood Clues

Here are some examples of mood clues. As you search for mood clues, you will begin to think of many others that are unique to your own experience.

Mood Clues for depression —

- Not wanting to walk to the mailbox because it takes too much energy.

31

- Sleeping at least one hour more than usual for three days in a row.
- Dreading an activity or feeling bored with something you normally enjoy.
- Craving sweets. (Anyone for chocolate?)
- Not wanting to answer the phone when a friend calls.
- Feeling diffusely overwhelmed.
- Looking only at the ground when walking.
- Feeling sad in the midst of doing something fun.
- Feeling anxious around other people.
- Feeling numb.
- Not having the energy to exercise.
- Failing to make eye contact.
- Noticing a marked increase or decrease in appetite.
- Questioning your ability to perform at work, even when things are going well.
- Difficulty remembering small things for several days in a row.
- Having trouble deciding what to wear for several days in a row.
- Losing your sex drive for several days.
- Feeling that life is not worth living.
- Thinking your friends don't like you any more.

Mood Clues for Mania —

- Starting several projects at once but not finishing any.
- Constantly feeling annoyed.
- Thinking that others are not keeping up with you.
- Feeling like you can't sit still.
- Not needing your usual amount of sleep for several days in a row.
- Wanting to have sex more often than usual or with partners you normally would not consider.
- Doing risky things just for the hell of it.
- Talking fast or changing subjects in the middle of a sentence.
- Being annoyed by sounds in your environment.
- Answering others with a sharp voice even though you are not angry.
- Not being able to stop for breaks while you are doing an activity.
- Feeling you have too much energy.
- Feeling highly driven to accomplish more than average in a short time.
- Becoming annoyed at any distraction from what you are doing.
- Becoming impatient while standing in line even though you have plenty of time.
- Having trouble listening to another person because you are doing all the talking.

- Making purchases that seem necessary but which you normally wouldn't make at all or without planning ahead.

- Becoming distracted by small interruptions that normally wouldn't bother you.

NORMAL MOOD AND MOOD CLUES

For two reasons, it's important to learn to recognize the set point of normal mood. First, it helps us understand bipolar disorder. Second, it leads us to identify critical mood clues so we can respond to them with resiliency skills to keep our mood on target more often. At first we find it difficult to see how being outside the mood zone of normal is affecting us. In fact, we may not even recognize normal mood although it's staring us in the face! However, with careful observation we can begin to perceive subtle changes in our mood before mood gets badly out of control.

Ever had your brakes go out on your car? At first, you sense a few subtle clues such as the brakes not responding as usual. Then perhaps you hear a squeak when pressing the brake pedal. Finally, you hear a grinding sound of metal grating against metal indicating the shoes are gone. You're too late! Recognizing the more subtle clues of brake failure would have spared you the bother and expense of a brake replacement. New brake shoes could have done the job!

Similarly, if we can recognize the subtle signs of mood change early — the mood clues — we can take steps to prevent serious problems. Our brakes don't have to give out completely before we fix them. And our moods don't have to become full-blown episodes before we address mood clues with recovery skills. *Discovering mood clues is essential in playing the game of bipolar disorder.*

SWEAT THE SMALL STUFF

Usually in life we are told, "Don't sweat the small stuff". With bipolar disorder the big stuff of mood episodes can be so overwhelming that, if we concentrate on them, it is hard to know where to begin. We can still see the big picture of episodes, hospitalizations, work issues, relationships and the ability to manage stress, but we focus on manageable mood clues.

On a day-to-day basis (and especially when we are very ill), it can be even more helpful to "sweat the small stuff". Mood clues can help us respond in small ways that will eventually teach us to regulate mood closer to the target of resiliency. As this happens we develop management and recovery skills that allow us to take over our moods and learn to live with bipolar disorder. *Discovering mood clues is essential in playing the game of bipolar disorder.*

OBSERVATION LEADS TO RESILIENCY

When I began to manage bipolar disorder in my own life, I discovered I needed to observe myself objectively to figure out where I was with the illness and in life. Without clarity about my experiences, I was left to cope without a pathway to resiliency and mental wellness. Observation has helped me recognize mood clues, and the process has given me a means of setting and achieving goals for mental wellness.

To recognize mood clues, it is helpful to observe ourselves and others. When you begin to do this, you may be surprised that you have had little insight into the fluctuations of mood you have been dealing with. It helps you better understand your life of mood as well as the impact it has had on your life.

When we begin to observe ourselves in ways that boost our recovery efforts, it's important to refrain from finding fault or focusing on undesirable traits. Faultfinding and self-deprecation are not what observation in recovery is about. A recovery perspective is one of searching for mood clues so we can take positive actions toward resiliency and recovery.

More importantly, observation enables us to respond to mood clues when they first appear in order to avert an episode. For those times when we are already entrenched in an episode, observing mood clues can help us get our sights off the overwhelming larger picture and begin to take small steps to manage bipolar disorder. *Discovering mood clues is essential in playing the game of bipolar disorder.* Observation takes us into the game with skills to help us win.

EARLY CLUES OF CHANGING MOOD

To begin searching for mood clues, observe your actions, thoughts and feelings. It may help to write the mood clues you notice in a notebook. I can't tell you what your earliest mood clues will be because they're different for each person , but as an example, here are some of mine:

For depression —

- Feeling negative about the day.

- Thinking that others don't care about me.

- Wondering whether life is worth living.

- Experiencing fatigue even though I've had enough sleep.

- Feeling that everything takes too long and that life has slowed down.

For mania —

- Speaking in clipped sentences.

- Hearing sharpness in my voice.

- Becoming annoyed over small things.

- Speaking rapidly.

- Desiring to stick with a project without breaks even when I'm getting upset about it.

- Losing tolerance for music or noise in the room.

Your mood clues may be completely different from these. Through diligent observation, you'll develop your own personalized list. If you're having trouble discovering your clues, start with a symptom such as the extreme fatigue of depression. Work your way back from a time when you became immobilized with this fatigue. Review whether the fatigue gradually increased. Ask yourself when you first noticed feeling just a bit "off."

With bipolar disorder, there are many times in which there are few or no mood clues. We just wake up and our mood has changed. When this happens, the sooner we are aware of the change, the sooner we can put resiliency skills into practice. At other times we gradually move toward a change in mood or toward an episode. These are times when observing early mood clues can allow us to intervene more quickly.

Having trouble recognizing clues? Ask others to help you. Someone close to you may recognize the clues before you do. They may say, "It's that certain look in your eye. I noticed it when I asked you whether we could go out to supper." Can you remember what that "look" was or what you were feeling?

You may even see clues in the behavior of others. Perhaps they leave the room because they don't want to be near you when you explode. Work your way back from that time and see if you can remember any mood clues that preceded that incident. Doing so may be difficult at first, but you will get better as you practice. To go *beyond bipolar*, persist, because *discovering mood clues is essential in playing the game of bipolar disorder.*

A NOTE TO FAMILY AND FRIENDS

In telling my readers to look for specific mood clues and to recognize them early, I am not talking to you! In fact, it is common for family and friends to become hyper-vigilant and to see each little mood clue as an indication that a crisis is brewing. This puts a heavy burden on you and on the person with bipolar disorder. If you react to or comment frequently about your observations, it can lead to a perception that you have focused solely on your loved one's illness.

Your job is to help your loved one retain self worth and their concept of a whole person who is loved and who can achieve life dreams and goals. Your focus need not be on mood clues but rather on giving support and help in problem solving when asked.

You may have fears and concerns of another episode that could lead to hospitalization, job loss, or even suicide. Your fears are valid and just as important as any of the issues covered by this book. However, becoming hyper-vigilant can push the one you love away from you. It may feel to them that they are living in jail, with each action being evaluated for breaking the rules. Vigilance is important, especially when there is suicide risk, but becoming hyper-vigilant can make you over-respond to small things and use up all your energy instead of saving it for the true emergencies.

Above all, your top priority should be to take care of yourself. When there is an airplane emergency, you put on your own oxygen mask before helping another person. That way you do not pass out before being able to give help. The same is true with bipolar disorder, which exacts a heavy toll on families and friends.

If you want to help the person you love, take care of yourself first. Be careful about focusing too much on another person's illness. You didn't cause it, and you, no doubt, would do everything possible to make it go away. If bipolar disorder becomes the sole focus of your life, you will not be able to bring a different focus to your loved one. Pay attention to bipolar disorder, but don't let it take over your life.

You have an immense challenge to your relationship. You may share the illness of bipolar disorder, or you may find its mood clues and episodes unfathomable. Either way, realize there are seldom enough sign posts put along your way that help you stay on the path. Your suffering is real, as is your sense of confusion at all that is happening.

Learn all you can about bipolar disorder. Get help from others, including counseling from trained clinicians and support from others who face bipolar disorder in their families. Be a hope carrier. Try to back away from your strong feelings in order to do objective problem solving. Apply the principles of this book to yourself and your own experience of living with bipolar disorder, even if you don't have the diagnosis. All of these actions will help get your oxygen mask in place so you can help the person you love.

I have struggled with the challenges of bipolar personally and as a family member of one who was diagnosed at an early age. I know that there are no easy answers to these challenges. And I also know that none of us need to be answering these challenges alone.

It takes courage to ask for and utilize help. I've known some family members who search for help like a barracuda, many of whom find what they look for against all odds. Others go it alone. Some are overwhelmed by guilt. Others distance themselves from the challenge. Some experience the loss of a loved one with bipolar disorder and set out on a different journey of grief.

If you think you can deal with this disorder without education, support, and problem solving skills, I believe you are wrong. I urge you to seek all the resources that are available to you. Above all, make your first priority taking care of yourself so you will be able to help your friend or family member as well as maintain other relationships that are important to you.

FAMILY OF MINOR CHILDREN AND ADOLESCENTS

If you are the parent or relative of a minor child, your approach might be to help your child understand the principle of observation. Your goal might be to help your child recognize mood clues and develop a plan to deal with them. Your child needs to gradually learn resiliency principles and recovery skills.

The long-term goal is that your child becomes an adult who can manage the challenges of bipolar disorder. To achieve this goal, you begin by modeling activities that are appropriate responses to illness. Next you gradually help your child become responsible for managing the challenges of bipolar disorder and needing only rare interventions from you or others.

Much as you would like to, you cannot take this illness from your child. If you try to substitute your own management of the illness without allowing your child to engage in active problem solving, your child will find it difficult to grow into adulthood with this disorder.

You may see your child as needing protection from having to deal with these issues, but remember, your child will be dealing with this disorder life long. As an example, many in the medical community used to think that children with diabetes could not manage their illness. Today the cutting edge treatment of children with diabetes teaches them to manage their illness from the earliest age possible.

Expectations are often a challenging issue, especially with older children, teens and young adults. Keep in mind any chronic illness almost always causes a delay and unevenness of developmental stages. Your child may be seventeen but playing like a twelve year old and yet responsible in going to work and school. Be patient when your fourteen year old is a straight-A student but acts like a ten year old around friends. Be patient when you child is having difficulty with school but shows initiative in other areas of life. Sometimes you have to strike a balance between recognizing the fourteen year old and accommodating the ten year old. With time, these developmental stages will even out and there will be catching up well into adulthood.

Watch Your Language

Be careful about the language you use. If I had cancer, you would never call me a cancer. Your loved one has bipolar disorder. Your loved one is not "bipolar". Bipolar disorder is not something we either "are" or "become". We are ourselves. We have a diagnosis of bipolar disorder.

It is common for family and friends to say of those with bipolar disorder (and of family members as well) that they are "in denial". May I suggest that they are in need of insight or that they need more information to understand the illness? The label of being "in denial" can feel like being put into a tiny, securely locked box. How does anyone get out of being "in denial"? Who decides when the person is out of that box? Is there even an opposite or reasonable alternative to being "in denial"?

SENTINEL MOOD CLUES

Using sentinel mood clues helps you respond to early changes in your mood. Observe for three sentinel mood clues for depression and three for mania. The word sentinel comes from root words meaning to feel or sense. Sentinel mood clues consistently appear preceding depression or mania. They are different for each person, but they can help you observe mood clues, just as a sentinel guard would watch for danger.

Note sentinel mood clues are specific. They don't necessarily indicate a full-blown depression, hypomania, mania or mixed mood. Rather, they're small mood clues about where your brain is taking you at the moment.

Sentinel Mood Clues Exercise

Follow these steps to identify sentinel mood clues:

1. To begin the Six Mood Clues exercise, make a long list of your own mood clues. Include at least eight to ten in your list. *(See pages 31-34 for some examples of mood clues if you are having trouble getting started.)*

2. As you become used to responding to mood clues, whittle this list down to sentinel mood clues, three for depression and three for mania. When shortening the list, key into things you can reliably observe when your mood begins to creep outside an acceptable range.

3. Watch diligently for these six mood clues. You now have a manageable way to recognize sentinel mood clues. The

list may vary at different times of your life. It's helpful to review your sentinel mood clues monthly or perhaps with the change of seasons to make sure they're doing the job you want.

This sentinel mood clue exercise allows you to individualize a recovery strategy of observation. As you practice it, you'll be able to identify mood clues and take action sooner each time they appear. Over time, responding swiftly to mood clues will help stabilize mood.

As an example, these were once my sentinel mood clues.

For depression —

- Sleeping an hour more than usual three days in a row.

- Not wanting to prepare meals two days in a row.

- Beginning to cry over things that normally wouldn't discourage me.

For mania —

- Having difficulty listening to others.

- Finding five or more books I had started reading but never finished.

- Becoming irritable to the point of a temper tantrum when things are difficult.

As I became more aware of my mood clues, and responded with resiliency skills, my mood became more stable. I no longer have temper tantrums on a regular basis as I used to. My sentinel list changed.

Today, it looks like this:

For depression —

- Feeling tired two to three days in a row without reason.

- Annoyed by having to do a simple task like preparing a meal or answering the doorbell because it feels like too much to do.

- Talking to myself in a discouraging way even though things are going well.

For mania —

- Noticing that my thoughts or speech are faster than normal.

- Seeing that I am distracted enough to drop a project in favor of another without thinking it through.

- Hearing sharpness in my voice that indicates I am becoming irritable even though I have not been provoked.

Your sentinel mood clues will change as you progress in your recovery plan. Their role will remain the same — to help you recognize mood clues so you can take action that will give you greater resiliency in managing bipolar disorder. Sentinel mood clues are a tool for observation. *Discovering mood clues is essential in playing the game of bipolar disorder.*

OBSERVE OTHERS!

We can take observation a step further by observing others as well as ourselves. Without doubt we will find people in our lives who also have the mood clues of depression and mania. But it is also useful to watch for the mood clues of normal mood in others.

I have watched people react to situations and asked myself

whether I would be reacting in a similar way. Whether my intense mood reaction or the other person's "normal" reaction is more helpful depends on the situation.

For instance, occasionally when driving I see a person who has been involved in a car accident. Traffic has slowed down in order to see the crumpled car but instead of focusing on the car, I watch the person who is calmly talking to the police officer, exchanging information with the other involved party and calling for a tow truck and a ride home.

In bipolar mode, I simply wouldn't react that way. I might find myself crying, yelling, pacing or doing any number of things that do not help take care of things. In observing others in the same situation, I can readily see that their response can include strong feelings of disappointment and even fear, but they are still able to take care of the situation without having to reign in their mood first.

In other circumstances, observing others may tell me that my "extra" range of mood might be an advantage. I may be able to present my ideas at a meeting in a more compelling way because I can choose to use the gift of a mood with more colors and shapes. This "extra" mood range can heighten my communication with others. It's one of the ways we express our passion for life to others.

Although we clearly cannot always make our mood fit any given situation, we can learn about moods and the possibilities of what we might want our mood to look like. To go *beyond bipolar*, we need to have as full an understanding of mood as possible. We experience such a wide range of mood that we don't always recognize that mood can take us beyond where we want to go. *Discovering mood clues is essential in playing the game of bipolar disorder.*

PACING WITH OTHERS

Observing others gives me a better understanding of the entire range of mood, including normal. It can also help me pace myself. Remember that mood is not just a matter of feeling. It involves much more, including our activities. In depression I can mobilize by upping my pace to match others around me for a short time. Doing this all day could be fatiguing, but doing it purposefully for a short time can help my brain realize that it needs to mobilize out of the slower speed of depression.

Likewise in mania, I can slow down a bit to match those around me. Instead of walking six steps ahead of my friend, I can intentionally slow my pace to give my brain the message that it needs to pull back a bit.

Another example is that of observing others in conversation. Comparing the rate of our thoughts to the rate of normal conversation can give us an opportunity to match another person's pace for brief periods of time by slowing down or speeding up. If you are like me, when your mind is working so much quicker than those around you, it is easy to comment internally on how slowly they are thinking and speaking. It is maddening to think of their slow pace, and I get impatient for things to move more quickly.

What it is difficult for me to understand in communicating my ideas or needs is that "normal mood speed" seems like a bottleneck to me. Sometimes the best way to clear a bottleneck is for me to slow down so I can adequately express myself. This allows others to get my message so I have been heard. This kind of bottleneck occurs frequently when we have racing thoughts. It is easy to think that others are just slow (or dense), but in reality, we are racing ahead of things.

Pacing with other's rates of conversation can impact our relationships. When we are racing, others are likely to react in a number of different ways. They may say, "Oh, that's Jane again with her funny ideas." This response doesn't require that they process my rapid-fire ideas. They may get angry and confused that I appear so impatient towards them. They may nod agreement even though they don't understand what I am trying to say. A rare individual will be able to ramp up their listening speed to stick with my barrage of ideas, but they are likely to fatigue before I will. Pace with others to get a sense of what "normal mood speed" really is. It will help you recognize mood clues. *Discovering mood clues is essential in playing the game of bipolar disorder.*

OBSERVE TO INCREASE ALTERNATIVES

With bipolar disorder, we can get pretty fixed on our own way of processing information and responding to our environment. In depression we can get mired down and tend to view the world and ourselves darkly. In mania we may think that our ideas are always better than those of others. The trouble is that when we live in the world of alternate moods, we don't often see other alternatives.

Observing others can help us to find out about the alternative of normal mood. One of the things that we can do is to observe others by listening for phrases and approaches that we might not ordinarily think of ourselves. To go *beyond bipolar* we will need to recognize, choose and practice feelings, thoughts and activities from those who live in that normal mood range. Remember, normal mood might not be our initial goal, but functional mood includes the normal range and doesn't go flying of to the extremes for long periods of time. *Discovering mood clues is essential in playing the game of bipolar disorder.*

Here's one alternative that recognizing mood clues gives us: we don't have to act on strong feelings. Instead we can think about other alternatives before we act. In observing others we will find some who are very good at problem solving. We can observe their process of mulling over problems with a careful, well thought out process rather than acting on strong emotions as our first reaction. We can pick up on phrases from others such as, "Let me think about this," or "I need to stop and think." When we see these working for other people, we can incorporate them into our toolbox of recovery skills.

When I am overwhelmed by my mind's suggestions that are taking me down the path to depression, I can say to myself, "I need to stop and think." In doing this I can refute the ideas that are swimming in my head. Part of this approach may be asking the question of what a reasonable person would think under the same circumstances. If I just got an A on a test and tell myself I didn't do well enough, would a reasonable person use the same line of reasoning? I don't have to draw the conclusion that I am not a reasonable person. Usually I am, but the moods of bipolar disorder can jog me off track.

Playing the Game to Win

A goal for everyone with bipolar disorder is to avoid major mood episodes, but true wellness involves far more than avoiding episodes. Wellness entails learning principles of resiliency and recovery skills that take us *beyond bipolar*. When we discover ways to make our quality of life what we want it to be in spite of bipolar disorder, we are winning the game. *Discovering mood clues is essential in playing the game of bipolar disorder.*

Here are some thoughts for you to consider in searching for mood clues:

1. Does it seem to you that your mood changes without any warning? How does it make you feel when you wake up in a certain mood? Does your sense of yourself change without insight into where the change comes from?

2. Although you experience moods that seem to come out of no where, do you think there could be mood clues that help you anticipate these changes or at least recognize them sooner?

3. Are your moods so strong that you feel they are in control of you? Do you think that, in spite of it being impossible to change your mood, you could react in small ways to mood clues rather than wait until they become episodes?

4. Does your mood change abruptly? If your mood takes a dramatic change, do you wait weeks or even months for your next appointment, or will you consider intervening with a phone call to get help sooner, before the mood gets entrenched?

5. How do you react to both positive and negative events of your life? Are some of these reactions colored by the overlay of a specific mood? Can you identify the mood clues? When your reactions are different from what you would expect, might they actually be the mood clues you are seeking to recognize?

6. Can you back up from points that are really difficult for you in order to discover mood clues? Imagine the feelings and activities that preceded your mood getting so out of control. Where mood clues missed? Can you list several responses that could have taken you off this path?

7. Do you understand that our brains can go to the extremes of mood regulation, but they can also wander in small ways? Do you see how dealing with mood clues may be easier than reacting to an episode as a whole?

Connect!

Depression and mania are connected by mood regulation.

D EPRESSION, HYPOMANIA, MANIA AND MIXED MOOD seem so different from each other that we often miss the fact that they are related to each other. The core feature of bipolar disorder is the brain's inability to consistently regulate mood within a normal range.

By looking at bipolar disorder as a whole instead of as individual episodes of depression or mania, we can recognize that the farther mood wanders from normal in any direction, the farther it can stray in another direction. In other words, a severe mania can lead to a deeper depression, or the other way around. *Depression and mania are connected by mood regulation.*

Here, and in the rest of this book, the word "mania" describes hypomania as well as mania. We can think of mood or mood clues as being on the mania or the depression side of normal. We don't have to make a distinction between hypomania and mania because the resiliency skills for both will be the same.

Mixed mood has mood clues or symptoms from both sides of

normal occurring at the same time. Here we take each mood clue or symptom separately. If it's on the mania side of normal, we'll use resiliency and recovery skills for mania. If it's on the depression side of normal, we'll use resiliency and recovery skills for depression.

The bipolar disorder I experience is characterized by more depression than mania. Because of this, I used to try to avoid depression, but didn't realize that paying attention to mania is equally important. Once I learned the secret of managing mood clues and symptoms on both sides of normal, I found a way to tame my depressions. In fact, I think that extra attention to the mania side of normal has helped me the most to prevent depression. To go *beyond bipolar* we need to realize *depression and mania are connected by mood regulation.*

CONNECTING DEPRESSION AND MANIA

Depression and mania are connected by mood regulation. Paradoxically, the moods of bipolar disorder have a close connection to each other. After extreme mania, depression can be deep. This may be hard to see because we experience discrete episodes of depression and mania.

If we return to the primary characteristic of bipolar disorder — the brain's inability to consistently regulate mood within a normal range — it makes sense that one mood can lead to another. When regulation isn't working, bipolar disorder can plunge you into depression or lift you into mania — often foreshadowed by mood clues of one or the other or even both.

The regulation of mood can be like a rubber band. When it is relaxed it stays in a circular or oval shape, which represents normal mood. If we pull the rubber band between the fingers of both hands and let go, it can snap and fly across the room in one direction or the other. When our mood stretches into mania, it can later snap into depression. Likewise, when our mood stretches into depression, it can then snap into mania. The more it is stretched in one direction, the farther it will snap in the opposite direction. If we hold the rubber band taught, without letting go, that's similar to a mixed mood. It's pulled in two different directions and doesn't have the relaxed shape of the rubber band at rest.

Pulling the rubber band with less force causes more relaxation and gets rid of the snapping. Resiliency and recovery skills help us regulate mood in a similar way so it has fewer extremes and is like the rubber band in relaxation. We learn to control mood as we would a rubber band to keep it closer to its normal, resting state. To go *beyond bipolar* we need to see the connection. *Depression and mania are connected by mood regulation.*

USING MOOD CHARTS

Mood charts are used to plot your mood on a scale one or more times during the day. Mood charts can be quite elaborate, especially if you include lists of your medications as well as notes about the day. In fact, you could get extremely involved in keeping a mood chart, but you don't have to. It can be done quite simply.

Many clinicians urge you to use mood charts because they provide a snapshot view of what's happening with your mood. These snapshots help decide what medications to prescribe or to make adjustments. Although this is a good strategy, I suggest you use mood charts in another way — to help observe the moods and mood clues you experience. The discovery of mood clues then prompts action on your part to apply resiliency principles and use recovery skills.

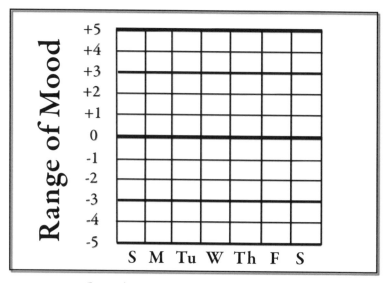

Plus/Minus Mood Chart

Mood charts come in all forms. Some have a scale in which zero (o) represents severe depression and ten (10) represents extreme mania. Some use a scale up to 30 or more points. Others make use of pictures instead of numbers to describe mood. These are often used for children but can be useful for adults who are young at heart. Mood charts can be called by various names including mood graph and mood diary.

You can find mood charts on the Internet by doing a search on "mood chart". You can also make your own. The most important thing is that you like the format of the chart you use and that it's not overly complicated.

Above is a sample of a mood chart. In this chart, zero (o) is normal (or what you think might be normal). Minus five (-5) is as depressed as you have ever gotten — so depressed that you might need to be in the hospital. Plus five (+5) represents extreme mania requiring hospitalization or a mania that is the highest you experience.

People who've never used mood charts can find them challenging at first. They often say they aren't sure where their mood lies. At first, most people with bipolar disorder have difficulty reading mood clues until the clues become intrusive into their lives. This is okay; your mood chart assessment doesn't have to be totally accurate in order to be helpful. The key is that you are observing mood clues to see where your actual mood would fall on a scale or chart.

If this is the first time you have asked yourself where your mood is along a continuum, it could be difficult to pick a number. You may want to choose more than one point to chart your mood. For example, to describe mood, you could mark minus two (-2) and plus three (+3) at the same time. (It's possible to have mood clues of depression and mania at the same time.) Suppose you're experiencing decreased hope (-2) and high energy (+3) at the same time. This may not represent an episode of mixed mood, but it's still an indication of where your mood is. It is especially helpful as an indication your mood may be about to change directions.

It can be helpful for you to briefly state the mood clues you have used to determine your mood should be assigned a higher or lower number. Don't get too bogged down with this exercise. There are no right or wrong answers. If it's difficult to peg a number for your mood, choose a number that might be close and move on with your day. The object is not to perfectly graph your mood, but rather to begin observing your mood life more carefully so you can begin to manage mood clues.

Different points on the chart may be appropriate for different times of the day. This is especially true for children who are ex-

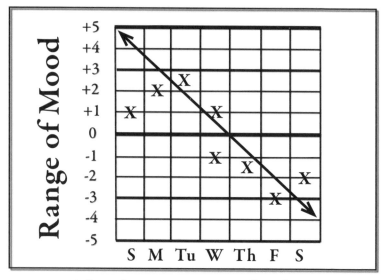

Plus/Minus Mood Chart

periencing rapid mood changes, called switching. Switching is a common experience in children who have bipolar, but it also occurs in some adults, especially perimenopausal women.

Try marking your mood chart once or twice a day for several weeks. If you forget to use your chart at times, simply go back to it when you remember. If you frequently forget to take medications, you may want to note the pills you're taking and when. Perhaps your chart can serve as a reminder. (Or, if you are consistent in taking medicines you can use your medication times to remind you to use your mood chart.) Put your chart in a convenient place that will remind you. Perhaps a note on your bathroom mirror or on your computer screen will work for you.

The chart above is an example of how to fill out a mood chart. The arrow helps us see the relationship between depression and mania. Remember, your goal is to get in tune with mood and to recognize the connection between depression and mania. You may also want to show your chart to your doctor or clinician, but mainly you're keeping it to observe yourself and make changes that help you manage bipolar disorder. At first your observations may lean toward the subjective side, but with practice you will be able to objectively observe moods and mood clues.

Often you will find that after keeping a mood chart for a while, you understand mood clues better. You can then respond by applying recovery skills sooner when your mood is becoming unstable. The mood chart may become unnecessary once you are adept at recognizing mood clues. Or you may want to pull it out during times when you are finding extra challenges in managing mood clues, perhaps when mood has gotten into a place where you feel it is controlling you rather than you controlling it. The idea is to see the connection. *Depression and mania are connected by mood regulation.*

REGULATING MOOD, NOT OVERCOMING IT

To achieve mental wellness, make mood regulation your focus. That means learning principles and skills that regulate mood. Therefore, the goal is no longer overcoming episodes of mania or depression; rather, it's regulating mood into a comfortable and functional place.

If your mood wants to take on a life of its own, reinforce the fact that you have your own life to live. When you find new ways to regulate mood, your brain won't constantly go to extremes. You'll minimize both the major flares and subtle mood shifts. How? By recognizing and managing mood clues early on, it is easier to stay within a reasonable range. Through regulation, your mood becomes resilient and keeps you from swinging too far in one direction. *Depression and mania are connected by mood regulation.*

ROLE OF MEDICATIONS

When you get treatment for bipolar disorder, you may feel much better taking one (or more) medications called mood regulators. At first, you can be tempted to keep your eye on episodes rather than mood regulation. But as you feel better, you experience normal or close to normal mood to function fairly well.

Later, when your medicine is working, it may seem reasonable to stop taking it. After all, who wants to take medications when you're feeling well? Keeping your eye on mood regulation instead of episodes of depression or mania helps answer this question. If you feel better while you're on medications, remember why. The rubber band of mood is not so taught and it is not snapping too far into mania or depression. *Depression and mania are connected by mood regulation.*

No matter where your mood is — whether it's in normal, depression or mania — focusing on regulation is the aim. The medications don't work just to alleviate extreme episodes; they work to keep the rubber band from getting stretched out of shape so it stays relaxed in a comfortable mood in or near the normal range. Unfortunately, countless individuals stop taking medications, often without consulting their prescribers. As a result they have learned by bitter experience that the consequence can be further episodes of depression and mania.

Regulation of mood is a lifelong challenge for those of us with bipolar disorder. That's why we need to give our brains the help they need to keep mood regulated within a reasonable range. Medication is a crucial tool. Treatment focuses on mood regulation over the long term because it helps the brain regulate mood consistently, not just when treating single episodes of depression or mania. *Depression and mania are connected by mood regulation.*

Dysphoric vs. Euphoric Mania

Have you ever felt you were so irritable that you could crawl out of your skin? In mania some of us feel dysphoric, which means we are extremely uncomfortable. Others of us feel astonishingly superb — the euphoric side of mania. But as mania is fueled by an ever-increasing energy, it frequently becomes dysphoric. Dysphoric mania can be characterized by intense irritability or an energy that keeps us restless even when we are dog-tired. The internal drive of amplified energy can be barely noticeable, but constant like a splinter.

Mania is so often described as feeling good that we often miss its mood clues when it's dysphoric rather than euphoric. Recognizing the mood clues of irritability early allows us to take action that enables us to move beyond exhaustion.

MAKING THE CONNECTION

Resiliency is about focusing on mood regulation rather than keeping your eye on the depression, hypomania, mania or mixed mood. This is a different way of looking at bipolar disorder from what most of us have been taught. To go *beyond bipolar* to mental wellness, we need to make the connection.

Here are some questions to help you see their relationship:

1. Do you remember the feeling when you were in depression or mania that no other mood existed for you?

2. Can you see any pattern to your moods? Does depression

follow hard on the heels of mania or hypomania? Does mania grow slowly or hit you all at once?

3. Which is more prominent in your illness — mania or depression?

4. Do you know of times in your life when you couldn't tell what your mood was — depression or mania? Could you have been experiencing mixed mood?

5. Have you experienced switching (changing mood suddenly) or rapid cycling (switching moods within a day, week or more than four times per year)?

6. Are you beginning to see that the moods of bipolar disorder are related to each other and that the common denominator is the regulation of mood?

Step 6

Mobilize!

Activation provides a way to escape depression.

PERHAPS MY GREATEST CHALLENGE during depression is that I am slowed down to the point of being stuck. This prevents me from problem solving and moving on with my life. Often I find beginning an activity to be most difficult. Depression seems to put a damper on the part of my brain that initiates activity.

Sometimes my brain gets so stuck thinking about dreary thoughts that I am removed from the realities of my life. In depression, my energy decreases and, even if I continue my daily activities, I find it more difficult to stay focused. I've found, however, that after spending a short time in this vegetative, less productive mode, I need to get back on the move.

Resiliency principles aren't magic. Sometimes I need the help of others to light a fire under my lethargy, but I also try to get myself going on my own for those times when nobody seems to be handy with a match. To go *beyond bipolar* toward a functional mood, mobilize in depression. *Activation provides a way to escape depression.*

UNDERSTANDING THE SPECTRUM OF DEPRESSION

The deep end of the depression spectrum is the extreme slowing down of energy that occurs both mentally and physically. It's when you place your energy level at zero or less than zero. Not all of us descend to this level of inertia, even though we may experience serious depression. At the shallow end of the spectrum, the low energy of depression is subtle. Because it's less dramatic, we may not realize it is happening until depression grips us firmly in its vise.

When you've been deeply depressed or experiencing the extreme lethargy of depression, getting out of bed may be one of the most challenging things you do. During these times, it's important to remember that the cause of this slowdown is depression itself. It doesn't mean you're lazy or don't want to be active normally.

Feeling the slowdown of depression has nothing to do with your character. Instead, it relates to the part of your brain that controls movement. When depression signals the brain to slow down, it's called psychomotor retardation. That means your brain (psycho) is telling the part of you that controls movements (motor) to slow down (retardation). "Retardation" here refers to a slowing of your ability to get going and move.

It's difficult to get moving when you're experiencing psychomotor retardation. Fortunately, getting started or initiating movement of any kind is often enough to activate you. I know a woman who says that when she feels this way, getting up to brush her teeth is enough to propel her into the shower and then on with her day in spite of feeling sluggish. Still, mustering up the strength to brush her teeth is a major struggle!

When you're at the shallow end of the depression spectrum, some simple tasks become difficult chores. For example, fixing a meal for yourself may seem to take too much energy even though you're continuing most of your usual daily activities. In fact, you may be doing all your usual activities but taking longer to complete them or feeling more fatigued than usual in the process. Perhaps your thoughts have slowed down or it's difficult to concentrate. Or maybe you have a barrage of thoughts but they are painting a picture of despair and discouragement.

In spite of keeping up your usual activities, you are exhausted most of the time, your thoughts go to suicide, or you return from work or a volunteer project feeling so tired that you burst into tears. Your work in the home suffers as well. This kind of depression can be made especially difficult when those around you don't realize where your mood has taken you. Do you ever function well and are told that nothing is wrong with you even though you are feeling overwhelmed with depression?

Those of us with bipolar disorder often can hide this kind of depression from other people. Talking about depression can make other people uncomfortable, and we are sensitive to that. Because we feel it's socially unacceptable to have depression, we must become actors in our public life. (It's no surprise that so many people with bipolar disorder choose acting as a career — we can be polished actors without ever going on stage!) We cover up how we actually feel, fooling those around us and sometimes hiding our sagging feelings so well that we fool even ourselves and miss the mood clues of depression. *Activation provides a way to escape depression.*

MOBILIZING BY INITIATING ACTIVITIES

Managing in times of depression can be extra challenging. Gone are the romance of mania and its energy and we are left with the dregs of bipolar depression. Initiating activities becomes a task larger than climbing Mount Everest.

Depression can get us stuck. For example, although we have a long list of things to do, we can't get started on anything. We want to join our friends for an outing, but the part of our brains that initiates activities of all kinds has fallen asleep and we just can't see a way to get going.

Mobilization involves just getting started. Whenever I notice the first mood clues of depression, I think of something to get me moving. I may feel slow as a tortoise, but I pick up that reptilian leg and shake it. My goal here is to move, not necessarily to accomplish a task. It's to overcome the depressive mood clues by mobilization. Purposefully initiating a small activity can be the starting point of increased mobilization.

I keep a list of minor things to do when I'm feeling this way I get low priority projects done, things like cleaning my desk or deleting old email. Usually I would tackle larger projects like writing this book, but when I am feeling depressed these smaller projects get me going without being overwhelming and making me easily discouraged. They also make it possible for me to say I accomplished something. Often five to ten minutes of smaller projects will enable me to move something larger. Mobilization, even in small ways, helps overcome the inertia of depression. *Activation provides a way to escape depression*!

UPPING THE ANTE

Match your activities with your level of depression and then step them up one notch at a time. Once you've matched your activities with your level of depression, up the ante just a little bit by adding a different mobilizing activity. For instance, if you're having difficulty getting out of bed, make your goal to get up and take a shower. Even though this may be all you do, it's an improvement over staying in bed all day. Next make the bed. If at first you roll back into bed, at least your bed will be made up.

You've gotten up, taken a shower and made the bed. Now add going for a walk around the block or doing ten minutes of gardening or five minutes of cleaning the kitchen. As your energy returns (and perhaps just ahead of its return), up the ante again by an incremental amount. Try to stay just a bit beyond your comfort level in depression by mobilizing. Your energy will rarely go from depressive energy to normal energy in a short time, but you can continue to use this strategy in small ways throughout the day.

Note that this "upping the ante" is more than just going through the motions of each day; it is a conscious decision to activate. To begin, only attempt small activities. Pretty soon it will become a way of life to "up the ante" in order to keep you moving toward the goal of mental wellness. While it may help to seek others to encourage you in this process, only you can decide to mobilize yourself.

If you're on the shallow end of the depression spectrum, you can still match your activities to your level of depression. Perhaps an eight-hour workday is already challenging enough. Don't prolong your day or add extra activities in the evening except when absolutely necessary. Instead add the technique of frequent, short breaks but keep the "up the ante" activity as well.

When you are experiencing depression but are able to continue your daily activities, activation can consist of small but frequent activities that punctuate your day. Walking briskly to the water cooler, pausing to visualize or take deep breaths, initiating a short interaction with another person are all ways to activate.

Here's a visualization technique that can be done in just a few seconds: Imagine something large and cumbersome like a locomotive. See the engine working intensely to get started. Bit by bit it increases in speed and as it speeds up a hill it seems to shrink and then races off the track and into the sky until it disappears, floating like an eagle.

In this kind of depression, your brain can become exhausted by your usual activities. When the brain gets tired, the more frequently you rest it the less time it takes to refresh it. In most work environments and in society in general, we expect to keep pace lest we be deemed a slacker or lazy. In reality, small and frequent breaks for our minds can be energizing and help to provide the activation we need in depression.

In using this kind of brain rest, you can "up the ante" even further by gradually increasing the time between breaks. Remember, mobilization in depression is different from grinding yourself into the ground when you have things to accomplish. You may want to decrease the number or length of things you do in depression. This will allow you to mobilize during the time you are engaged in activities. *Activation provides a way to escape depression.*

Work Accommodations

When you begin to notice subtle mood clues of depression is the time to consider accommodations at work. Perhaps you can go into work a bit early and then take a longer break for lunch or, even better, take shorter but more frequent breaks. Can you do part of your work at home where you can space it out with more frequent breaks or will it harm your ability to follow though and to keep your home life reasonably separate from your work life?

If you need to meet with others, can you accomplish the same task with a couple of short phone calls instead of a formal meeting that requires intensive preparation? To learn about other accommodations, contact the Job Accommodation Network at 800-526-7234 or 877-781-9403 (TTY) or see their website at www.jan.wvu.edu.

In applying accommodations at work, remember that most will be short term and only during the time that you are feeling depressed. Some permanent changes such as having a quiet workspace away from the madding crowd are not for pulling yourself out of depression but for helping you maintain a stable mood.

In order to have protection and accommodations under the Americans With Disabilities Act (non-federal employees with 15 or more employees) or the Rehabilitation Act (federal employees), you will need to tell your employer that you have a disability covered by the act and suggest appropriate accommodations. Disclosing a disability may put you at risk since many employers will not know how to utilize this information to your and their benefit. Discrimination, lapses of confidentiality and stereotyping are possible outcomes.

Whether to disclose a disability is not a spur of the moment decision. Do your homework ahead of time by seeking help from a disabilities specialist and be prepared so that you can lead the discussion toward appropriate accommodations that are inexpensive for your employer and that benefit your company's bottom line as well as your health. Consider whether disclosure might lead to irreparable harm to your reputation. In an ideal world, this would never be the case, but we are still living in a society where psychiatric illness is maligned and misunderstood.

However, many people with bipolar disorder lose their jobs and the ability to work without first becoming educated about accommodations. Obtaining the best outcome requires becoming educated about your rights and the risks of exercising these rights.

ASSESSING EXPECTATIONS

In depression, we often set higher goals than are reasonable and we feel worse than ever when we don't accomplish our goals. Our expectations are skewed and do not allow for the depression we are experiencing. Expectations others place on us can also become a challenge.

Many of us take time off when we're sick with a bad cold. If we had diabetes and our blood sugars were too high or too low, we might take a day or part day off work to get stabilized. So why can't we take some time to take care of ourselves during times of depression? Most of us would say that we're being lazy or we would feel too anxious or too much pressure. In fact, if we don't already believe this, people around us may tell us so!

Clearly, bipolar disorder is challenging to live with. To take care of ourselves, we occasionally need downtime to focus on the challenge of depression. It seems so much easier to ignore our symptoms and mood clues, but taking care of ourselves means addressing issues when they occur. Note that downtime is not the same as going to bed and staying there for six weeks. Our downtime needs to be directed toward taking care of ourselves daily, hourly, and even minute-to-minute. Downtime is mobilizing that occurs away from our usual activities.

Downtime for depression helps us manage our symptoms so we can get better. During downtime, we may rest more than usual, but we still mobilize because to escape depression, we need to mobilize! Take two or three short walks during the day, work on psychotherapy skills and eat healthy foods. Use some of your day off to prioritize your activities. As you feel better, you can add projects until you get back to your full capacity.

Why is it important to review expectations during downtime?

In depression, we tend to see ourselves as not good enough. We may respond by increasing our responsibilities to make ourselves feel that we are worthwhile. It is equally defeating to assess our accomplishments in a negative light. Unfortunately, doing so builds unrealistic expectations. When we fail to meet these expectations, we question our value. That's when we might give in to the hopelessness that often accompanies depression.

Assessing expectations in depression is one more way of mobilizing. This may sound strange because I am asking you to decrease your expectations at the same time I'm telling you to mobilize. Think of it like simmering something on the stove by applying constant heat at a lower level instead of turning up the heat to let it boil over. In depression, keep the low heat of mobilization on simmer rather than turning it up all the way. You are running a marathon, not a sprint. Don't waste your energy all at once, but steadily apply it throughout the day and slow down enough to regain your forward motion when your energy lags. By doing this you will go *beyond bipolar* toward healthy mobilization. *Activation provides a way to escape depression.*

ADDING STIMULATION

In depression we frequently withdraw and become increasingly isolated. We want to go to bed, curl up in a fetal position and pull the covers over. In doing so we can become immersed in a totally non-stimulating environment. Here our minds fall asleep or ruminate on depressive thoughts.

If we have family or friends who are concerned about our inactivity, they may try to stir us up by suggesting activities. Some of the activities they suggest may not contribute to activation, because often they are too intense and overwhelming. Going to a ball game or movie, cleaning up the house, or walking or running a mile is probably too exhausting and will not increase your overall energy.

Again, matching your activities to your level of depression and then gradually "upping the ante" is a better approach to activation. Listen to soft music, have a short conversation, or let the sun shine on your face for a few minutes. Increase the level of stimulation to a short walk, make a telephone call, and spend a brief time doing something you normally would enjoy.

When your depression lifts a bit, you might enjoy the ball game or movie. Then you can clean the house and get back to your regular exercise routine. Be patient with yourself but continue to "up the ante" with mobilization.

Ways to Take Care of Yourself

When you notice mood clues of depression, consider these things:

- Cancel a complicated social engagement to take care of yourself so you have energy for work or family or yourself.

- Prepare a simple meal instead of a gourmet feast. If you're having dinner guests, make it a potluck and ask guests to bring dishes instead of doing all the cooking yourself.

- Prioritize your activities by asking, "Does this really have to be done today or can it wait until next week?" Focus on the things that need to be done now.

- When someone asks you to do something, you can always say yes later if you truly want to do it. You might want to get back to them later. Or try stating you can complete the task in a couple of weeks rather than promising to finish it right away. A corollary to this is to learn to say "no". Words like "This won't work for me because…" might help, but whenever you say "no" to something, make it plain that "no" means exactly what it says.

- Take a power nap to help get back your energy. (If you relapse into hibernation when you nap, it will be healthier for you to stay awake during the day.) Since napping can disrupt nighttime sleep, try not to sleep more than eight hours total per day or the amount you personally require when you are feeling well.
- Chose one activity to work on at a time. Often in depression, we think of all the things that aren't being done because of our decreased energy; then we end up doing few to none of them. Instead, choose a small project or a small section of a larger project and stick with it until you're done.

GETTING DETAILED

When you're slowed down with depression, mobilize yourself by getting detailed. Begin by taking on one small project at a time and write all the steps required before beginning. When experiencing depression that slows you to a stop, the steps to brushing your teeth may include the following:

1. Go to the bathroom.

2. Find toothpaste.

3. Find toothbrush.

4. Repeat steps 2 and 3 as necessary.

5. Put toothpaste on brush.

6. Put away toothpaste — where it belongs.

7. Brush teeth.

8. Put away toothbrush — where it belongs.

9. Rinse mouth.

Don't even think of flossing! You already have nine things on your list. Add flossing as soon as you feel better.

Next, use a highlighter to mark off each of these nine steps as you do them. Use two or three colors if you wish. In the end, don't look at whether you did every item on your list. You may not have put away your toothbrush. Never mind. As a measure of your accomplishment, look only at the color on the page.

Let's say you're in school and have a paper due next week. Here's what you'd likely put on your list:

1. Review instructions for the assignment.

2. Decide on three possible topics.

3. If possible, chose one. If you can't decide, choose the topic you know most about, flip a coin a couple of times to eliminate two subjects or draw one topic out of a hat. The point is to make a decision.

4. Decide what kind of research you need to do.

5. Make a detailed list of how to do the research

6. Do the things on your "how to research" list

7. Finally, make a third list to begin the next part of the project — the writing.

Use a highlighter to mark through each item you accomplish on your list. Again, you may not finish everything today, but if you have color on your sheet of paper, you can see you've made progress. Celebrate your success with a special treat or simply tell a friend what you've accomplished.

You may be thinking that this exercise focuses on too many

details. If you also have a diagnosis of Obsessive-Compulsive Disorder, you may not want to try this, or if you do, have a therapist help you monitor how it's working. This exercise would be obsessive if you weren't having trouble mobilizing or if you used it for every little thing in your life, even when depression hasn't slowed you down. But as a tool for mobilization, it can get you going and take you *beyond bipolar* to activation.

Remember that people get stuck in depression when starting their activities. Blaming yourself for not accomplishing a project also immobilizes. Instead, take productive steps. Seeing color on a do-list shows you the progress you've made and reinforces your efforts. *Activation provides a way to escape depression.*

Asking, Then Doing

Here's another way to activate that has often helped me overcome the immobility of depression. I ask, "What would I be doing now if I weren't feeling depressed?" Then I do that thing.

This simple question helps me get past where my brain is trying to take me and removes my thoughts from the depressing subject. Here are some examples:

If I weren't feeling depressed I would…

- Call a friend.

- Go to a movie.

- Bathe and comb my dog.

- Run errands.

- Go to work.

- Write a book.

- Call a supportive relative.

- Take out the trash.

- Go swimming.

The "Ask, then do" process helps us initiate activity. When used with other recovery skills, initiating activities can help your brain regulate mood so you don't get so bogged down in depressive thoughts. The key in depression is to mobilize *beyond bipolar* to mental wellness. One way to mobilize is to ask, then do. *Activation provides a way to escape depression.*

GETTING ON THE MOVE!

It can be oh, s-o-o-o taxing to activate in depression. For me, this is the hardest principle to apply. I'm struggling with this as I write these words. Take courage and have hope. As you practice applying this principle, and as you recognize the mood clues of depression to take quicker action, you will obtain the desired results. Each time you struggle, it may be a new game in which you are facing a fierce enemy. Remind yourself to go back to the steps of activation. *Activation provides a way to escape depression.* Be patient with yourself but persistent in applying this principle.

Here are some things to consider that will help you mobilize:

1. What are the mood clues that indicate you need to begin to mobilize?

2. Do your depressions take you deeper into furious activity to keep your mind off your thoughts, or do you tend to shut down altogether?

3. Can you understand the concept of matching your activities to your mood in depression and then "upping the ante"?

Are there any examples in your own life that you can use to demonstrate this has helped you in the past? If this is a totally new concept for you, can you think of a way to use it today?

4. How would a detailed list help you with something you need to get done today?

5. Do you feel that mobilization is impossible when you are feeling depressed. If so, can you begin by mobilizing in your imagination before trying a mobilizing activity?

6. Is it easier or harder for you to mobilize when you are around someone else or with a group of people? How is taking a down day different from withdrawal from others?

Brake!

Slowing down provides an escape from mania.

TURNING TO MANIA, we see the primary resiliency principle is opposite to that of depression: it involves slowing down rather than activating. Mania is already an activated state. It is also a state that affects other moods. The more extreme mania becomes, the deeper the depressions that follow may be.

It always seems natural to me in mania to speed up rather than slow down. Here's how I think: "I've just been depressed and now I need to make up for lost time." Or perhaps: "I am truly creative and productive in mania, so I need to ride this energy while it lasts." With these thoughts, I take on all kinds of projects that are goal driven. Even if this isn't a conscious thought process, this is what naturally happens. Unfortunately these behaviors are over-stimulating so that they encourage taking mania to an extreme. As a result, I fuel my already activated mood.

Energy level also affects my thinking in this way: "I have energy so why not use it to its fullest? It's great to have energy." Eventually I exhaust myself and discover that overall I can be far more productive and have energy for longer periods of time when I apply the brakes. I don't have to stop completely, but a gentle pumping of the brakes throughout the day gives me the results I want — high productivity, energy and creativity.

When I begin to apply the brakes to mania frequently throughout the day, I learn that because depression and mania are connected by mood regulation, the depressions I experience are not as deep. Having gotten a handle on the brake pedal, I go *beyond bipolar* toward a level of mental wellness that I had been hoping to achieve. *Slowing down provides an escape from mania.*

LONG-TERM PERSPECTIVE

Adopting a long-term perspective helps us realize our need to stay in treatment and keep the focus on resiliency. This helps us resist the desire to go off medications when the fire of mania strikes. It motivates us to learn how put out the fire of mania — to quench rather than fuel.

As with fires, when dealing with mania, the smaller the episode, the easier it is to put out. That's why it's important to be aware of the first mood clues of mania and take action as soon as you observe them — just as you would with depression.

Gaining a long-term perspective helps us apply the high energy of mania toward achieving our long-term goals. Many say they are more creative when experiencing florid mania. The truth is that we are more able to transform creative ideas into reality when our moods are regulated within a normal range or at least close to a normal range.

With a long-term perspective we can see that the extremes of mania take considerable time out of our productive life by hospitalizations and distraction from our personal goals. If we don't experience the extreme of mania with hospitalization, we can still appreciate that since depression and mania or hypomania are linked, letting mania run its course unchecked leads to deeper and longer lasting depressions.

Mania may be fun at times but it is not a benign mood. Going *beyond bipolar* to mental wellness requires that we take a long-term perspective. This perspective gives insight into the fact that mania must be managed for us to live a mentally healthy life. *Slowing down provides an escape from mania.*

Doing Less, Not More

When your brain is bent toward mania, you may feel compelled to start more activities than usual. A tip-off for me is when I start reading five or six books. Then I find books all over the house that I've begun to read but haven't finished. Once I've started reading a new book, I often forget about the previous one and the ones before. The unstable mood of mania causes me to move from one thing to the next without finishing anything while my energetic self keeps taking on interesting projects in a rapid-fire fashion.

In the state of mania or when mood clues of mania are present, it's natural to want to do more — to be more — to make up for lost time. Added to that, we feel driven by the energy that is ever-present and ever-exhausting. Caution: this is exactly when it's important to decrease stimulation by slowing down your activities.

That doesn't mean that we can't use the high productivity of mania to our advantage. We just do it differently. For instance, with the early mood clues of mania, many of us decide to clean our homes, a positive and highly productive activity. If we've recently experienced depression, we likely have stacks of things to clean up!

I encourage you to do this activity if you choose. It's much more likely to be productive than doing other things that might be destructive. The key here is how you do it. The common tactic in mania is to attempt to clean the whole house in a couple of hours. The resiliency-focused way is to clean a small section, maybe only a part of a room. Complete a section then stop in order to briefly apply the brakes. For example, take five minutes to breathe deeply, imagine yourself slowing down or go for a brief, but slow walk. After one of these activities, you're ready to tackle cleaning another section of the room.

In effect, you are refusing to fuel the mania because you have the long-term perspective that a clean home isn't worth it if the price you pay for it is depression. The depression that follows is deeper in response to the height of the previous mania. Remember, mania and depression are connected through mood regulation. Slowing down in mania will also help you manage depression while fueling mania will worsen both.

Apply this principle of slowing down in mania to other projects as well. You'll discover that putting the brakes on mania actually allows you to be more productive. In my experience of applying this principle, productive periods last longer and I can enjoy high creativity and put it to its best use. *Slowing down provides an escape from mania.*

FUELING THE FIRE

I lived in Denver during a severe drought when the Hayman fire was burning 30 miles southwest of the city. The fire was a distance away but its fury extended to the center of Denver through the ashes that darkened the sky for days.

Over a period of several weeks, reports came in daily telling of firefighter actions that eventually quelled the fire completely. In the springtime conditions for flooding and mudslides were ideal. Out-of-control mania is like this forest fire. It spreads like wildfire into many aspects of our life.

The destructive elements of mania chase its euphoria — just like ashes, floods, and mudslides result from a forest fire. Even when depression doesn't follow mania, we're left with the challenge of putting our lives back together again.

Fueling mania is so common in bipolar disorder that it can be seen as a normal progression of the illness. It's like the wind stirring a forest fire. Remember, mania and depression are connected by mood regulation. Because they are linked, the higher the mania, the deeper the depression that follows. When we're experiencing mania, fueling the fire makes sense. However, the ashes and destruction can spread far and be difficult to clean up.

Even if a deeper depression doesn't result from an accelerated mania, the consequences of out-of-control mania can be devastating. They may include buying sprees, sexual indiscretions, and compulsions to keep moving in spite of an overwhelming fatigue. Jobs, relationships, and finances can be affected, not to mention involvement with the criminal justice system or even death from risk-taking behavior.

Even without extreme behavior, mania, when it has run its course, leaves a landscape of unfinished projects and continuing responsibilities from over-commitment. Mania may signal productive periods of our lives replete with goal-directed activities. But it may also include irritability that negatively impacts our relationships and sense of self worth over the long term. Once the forest fire of mania is put out, the residue of its fury still has to be addressed.

After a manic episode, our brain is primed for the flood of depression and the mudslides of despair. Even though the "fire" may seem awesome while it's burning, the destruction left behind includes deeper depressions or more parts of our lives to redeem.

If we experience a pleasant (euphoric) mania, we crave more of this exhilarating energy. The fire of mania grows ever larger until it takes on the proportions of a forest blaze. But just as forest fires leave behind devastation, we may experience much deeper depression due to the wind fanning mania's flames.

Remember, mania and depression are connected by mood regulation. Fueling even the early mood clues of mania will encourage mood regulation to get farther out of whack. *Slowing down provides an escape from mania.* It also has a positive impact on depression that may follow mania.

Hypomania and Bipolar Disorder, Type II

If you have bipolar disorder, Type II, it is important to understand that it is not a milder form of Type I. Too many people in the medical community make the same mistake. Life-long, Type II is characterized by deep depressions punctuated by episodes of hypomania. In Type II, it is easy to think that hypomania doesn't need to be dealt with aggressively because depressions are more characteristic of the illness. Indeed, episodes of hypomania can be welcome relief from the depressions. But since depression and the hypomania of Type II are connected through mood regulation, paying attention to the hypomanic side of the coin affects the depressive side.

Those of us with Type II are fortunate that we don't experience the extreme of mania, but we can be easily fooled into disregarding the consequences of irritability that causes us anguish and has a negative impact on our relationships. Slowing down in hypomania doesn't mean forsaking its positive attributes of high productivity. Rather, it means applying the brakes gently and regularly to slow us to a better pace with which we can utilize its energy.

When I learned to slow down during hypomania, depressions became more manageable and less frequent. A lifetime of deep, often suicidal depressions gradually gave way to resiliency with occasional depressions that are short and mild. It's still hard on the hypomania side of things to apply the brakes, but in my life this resiliency skill has had the greatest positive impact on my illness.

No matter what kind of bipolar disorder you experience, the resiliency principle remains the same—*Slowing down provides an escape from mania* (hypomania).

SLOWING DOWN

An effective way to regulate mania is to use your mind and body for slowing down. In mania, it seems as though the rest of the world has slowed down. Adopting a long-term perspective, you realize that it's you who is speeding up. Some refer to this as "getting real," which means to get more in sync with the real world by slowing down.

Here are ways you can do this:

- Walk slowly, taking notice of each step you take.

- Slow down your speech intentionally.

- Breath slowly and deeply for a short time.

- Sit still for up to five or ten minutes and don't allow yourself to move or talk. Do this three to five times a day. (This might be a tremendous challenge for you, but can really help slow down your rapid-fire, manic style.)

- When you're engaged in highly productive activities, set a timer for 15 minutes. When the timer goes off, stop what you're doing and take some deep breaths to slow down your mind and rest your brain. Gradually increase the time allotted until you discover a balance that leaves your mind and body feeling rested.

- Visualize something that has high energy and is moving at the speed of light. Then slow it down in your mind and transform it into something else that has less energy and speed. Finally visualize it stopping altogether.

The best time to apply these recovery skills is when mania is just beginning. That's why observation and noticing mood clues of mania are valuable skills to develop. When your forest fire is totally out of control, you may not be able to apply these slowing down skills without help. You've heard firefighters report that a fire is 10 percent controlled. Days later it may be 20 percent controlled, then 50 percent. Similarly, putting out the fire of mania can take time because it's a process. Instead of fueling the fire of mania, fight it as soon as you're able. *Slowing down provides an escape from mania.*

AVOIDING OVER-STIMULATION

When you decided to clean your home in a couple of hours, did you also turn up the music as loud as it would go? I'd be surprised if you didn't. It's a common way of fueling mania without realizing. As you know, loud music sounds great and adds more energy to your already high-energy experience. (You will easily recognize loud, energizing music as a marketing tool in many stores.)

Are the banner and pop-up ads on your computer especially

annoying when you have the irritability of mania? Even small things can be stimulating. With bipolar disorder, especially in mania, the brain doesn't do a good job of filtering stimulating triggers in our environment. We need to help it out by avoiding over-stimulation.

Once I was sitting on my front porch trying to read quietly to calm an exhausting, irritable hypomania. A robin was singing its heart out over a block away, defending its territory. I finally had to go inside as its strident song was triggering more and more irritability. Because my brain couldn't filter out its sharp call, it seemed to pierce right through my brain. The hypomania I was experiencing was being revved up a notch by this stimulation.

Concerts and video games also can be highly stimulating in mania. So can social events with their conversation and earsplitting music. In mania, even something as simple as a person talking to you in an excited manner can be over-stimulating.

Visual stimulation can also be a challenge in mania. The visual cortex in the brain can become activated so that darting flashes of light appear in the sides of the visual field and a bright color here or there will catch the eye. In mania, all kinds of visual detail may fuel the fire, including how we see colors. You know this if you've ever chosen colors to decorate your home while experiencing mania.

Does this mean we need to sit in dull-colored, quiet rooms as we while away the time in mania? No—instead we can use recovery skills to keep things in check. Here are some:

- Keep the amplifier, TV, or computer sounds lower than usual. Sure, turn up the volume for a few minutes if your favorite song is on, but when it's over, return the sound to a softer volume.

- Close doors throughout your home for quiet.

- Avoid highly stimulating activities or attend them with a plan to follow. If you want to go to a family party, football game, or concert, take steps to decrease the stimulation. Wear earplugs. Leave the party for several minutes throughout the evening. Attend the event but don't stay the whole time.

- When you find yourself in a stimulating environment, find a quiet place where you can escape frequently for five to ten minutes at a time.

- When shopping, make a list and go to small shops or grocery stores instead of huge outlets with swarms of people. Avoid or spend less time in stores that hype up the music to encourage buying. Shop at quiet times of the day. Shop online, but also watch for the hyper-stimulation of many web sites with all the bells and whistles. (Of course, avoid shopping altogether if "shopping" and "buying spree" mean the same to you when you are having mania.)

Over-stimulation can easily fool you. It can feel good in mania, but it fans the fire. To go *beyond bipolar* to mental wellness, try decreasing stimulation. This is an easy way to "slow down". *Slowing down provides an escape from mania.*

EXERCISING

Exercise is an excellent tool to use in mania because it helps you get your excessive energy under control. With so many available ways to exercise, you can always choose something that interests you. (CAUTION: Don't choose extreme sports that push you to your physical limits in times of mania since they cause an overproduction of some of the same neurotransmitters that are linked to mania.)

Begin exercise by forcing yourself to slow down. Then allow yourself to speed up and work off steam. Finally, make yourself slow down again. You can also punctuate exercise with periods of rest or slower speed. This is like applying the brakes by pumping them gently rather than screeching to a halt. With mania, gentle but consistent slowing down is the key. Your energy will not allow you to stop suddenly, but you can still pump the brakes occasionally.

Consider whether competitive exercise is helpful. If you're highly competitive by nature and competition heightens mania, you might choose a non-competitive activity. Alternately, you can continue with competition but curb your highly competitive edge during times of mania. Learn to have fun — even if you are not winning! If you are a competitive person as I am, the compulsion to win is especially strong. If you team up with others who play to win, be sure to observe sore losers and gracious winners. Try to get in step with the more positive players rather than accentuating emotional intensity following a loss.

If you normally don't exercise, start with a simple activity such as walking. Exercise doesn't have to last long to be an effective tool for managing mania. Taking a five-minute walk several times a day may be more effective than doing a continuous run. If you're in good physical condition and used to plenty of exercise, you'll probably chose a higher level of exercise to get the same results as someone who normally is less active.

As you walk or exercise, slow down your thoughts. Use the deep breathing of exercise to help you focus. Discipline your mind to concentrate on the exercise for a few minutes, and then alternate this with allowing your mind to wander.

When your creativity goes wild, pull it back with more exercise. This advice is not meant to squash your energy and creativity through exercise. Rather, it's a tool for harnessing some of it so you can accomplish your creative goals without fueling mania. *Slowing down provides an escape from mania.*

WALKING AWAY

Mania — especially mania associated with irritability — is countered with the recovery skill of walking away. When events get frustrating, "walk away" for a few seconds to get your focus.

Realize that you can "walk away" for a few seconds at work without even moving—even during a business meeting! No one will notice if you take a few seconds to take some deep breaths using your diaphragm and tummy. Remember to think about the air moving in and out. The key to this (and nearly all recovery skills) is to use them early when you notice the first mood clues of mania. A second key is to use recovery skills frequently throughout the day.

You may want to remove yourself physically from a situation or person when you become over-stimulated. If you find it difficult to problem-solve during times of mania, try strategizing in advance when you're not experiencing mania or when it hasn't yet become full blown.

To remove yourself from a meeting, take a bathroom break. If appropriate, look at your watch and state that you have another engagement. You might even suggest it's time for everyone to take a break. If the group takes a break, be sure to get away quickly from others for a few minutes to execute your original strategy of walking away.

If you're dealing with an inanimate object such as a frustrating computer, just say, "I'm walking away!" Then do it. For instance, I call my computer Freddie the New, so I just say, "Freddie, I'm walking away. You go to sleep. I'll be back in a couple of minutes to deal with you!"

Don't regard walking away as running away. In fact, if you walk away sooner rather than later, you'll be able to calm yourself more easily and more quickly. You can then return to the situation at hand with only a short interruption.

When the brain becomes fatigued as it does from the high energy of mania, you will feel better sooner if you rest it earlier. While it's hard to interrupt increased productivity and the intensity of mania, it becomes worthwhile as your moods even out. Putting the brakes on mania helps you go *beyond bipolar* toward mental wellness in your mood life. *Slowing down provides an escape from mania.*

Don't Fuel the Big TT

An unpleasant consequence of manic irritability is the Temper Tantrum ("the big TT"). You may feel better after a tantrum or rage but those around you don't. Catching irritability as soon as you observe its mood clues simply enables you to walk away sooner. Walking away can result in less irritability, while helping to maintain the increased productivity that can accompany mania. It also helps you avoid alienating the rest of the world and building up a load of guilt over a string of TT's.

If temper tantrums or rages are a part of your mania, remember that this is not the same as anger. Anger has a focus. The irritability that leads to the outbursts of mania is diffuse and can be aimed at nearly anything in your environment, releasing a flood of rage. If your family or friends (or the police) are asking why you are always angry, you need to understand the difference between anger and irritability. Making this distinction can help you recognize irritability earlier in order to deal with it before it is fanned into a rage or temper tantrum.

Early mood clues of irritability include sharpness in your voice, annoyance at small things and being critical about things that don't really matter. Eventually you feel as though you could crawl out of your skin. Deal with early mood clues of irritability with techniques such as deep breathing, briefly walking away or visualization exercises. The "crawl out of your skin" type of irritability is more challenging. Calm yourself by exercising or relaxing with a warm shower—even taking a half-day off work if you can manage it. If you take time off work and spend it bemoaning your work situation, that will not help tame your irritability. Instead use the time to quiet mania and to problem solve what you will do when you return.

Once you are enraged, it is difficult to stop yourself. If you have waited until then to start deep breathing, you've waited too long. When I get this irritable, it helps me to have someone in the room with me as a calm and quieting presence.

The goal is to learn to calm yourself when faced with irritability. Think of this as retraining the brain by giving it new tools. The first key is to recognize early on that you are becoming irritable. The second is to apply calming skills such as deep breathing. The third is to become so accustomed to using the calming skills that they kick in automatically. A crucial point is that you practice calming skills throughout the day, even when you are not feeling irritable.

In the end, there will be some temper tantrums and rages, but their frequency and fury can be diminished over time. When they do happen, they must be acknowledged and dealt with. Whether it is an apology and a request for forgiveness or picking up the items that were thrown around the room (house), you can still take responsibility and try to fix the consequences of your actions. Hopefully you have not physically harmed yourself or others, but if you have, you must seek professional help quickly.

Remember, it is not your fault that you are sometimes overcome by this illness. However, you are still responsible for taking care of its outcomes. If you wish for mental wellness and the community of others, you will see how important it is to be responsible for your actions even when they are triggered by your illness. Even when you are irritable, *slowing down provides a way of escape in mania.*

PACING WITH OTHERS

You can learn to pace your thoughts and activities by following the cues of those around you. For instance, in a conversation, if the person you're talking to speaks slower than you do, try matching their pace so you slow down. This technique also helps slow your thoughts as it brings the other person on board with your speech so you can be better understood. Remember, in mania, it is not the world that has slowed down, but your brain that has sped up.

Use this yoking technique when walking with another person, doing a project together, or playing a game. At first it will be difficult. To you, the other person is going so-o-o-o slowly. I suggest you try it for a few minutes at a time and then come back to it frequently throughout the day. Remember that the other person is probably functioning in real time, not manic time. This yoking works because *slowing down provides a way of escape in mania.*

BREATHING DEEPLY

Like in depression, deep breathing can help modulate the mood of mania. To be effective, do it frequently and use your belly. Hold one hand beneath your belly button and make sure that your hand rises and falls as you breathe from your diaphragm and abdomen. Additionally, hold your ribs out to allow your diaphragm and chest the greatest amount of space for breathing.

Here's how you can develop a slow rhythm. First inhale deeply with your belly moving out. Next hold your ribs out to complete the inhalation. Then move your belly in as you exhale slowly. Finish the sequence by allowing your ribs to return to a natural position at the end of your breath. Repeat these steps, trying to make the motions as slow and even as possible.

Here are the steps to follow in a condensed form:

1. Belly out while breathing in

2. Ribs out to finish inhalation

3. Belly in as you begin to exhale

4. Ribs in to finish exhalation

Many people with bipolar disorder take yoga lessons to learn breathing techniques and to receive the benefits of learning to relax. I suggest taking specific classes like yoga, meditation or singing to learn how to breathe from the diaphragm. You can also learn these techniques by taking a TV yoga class or checking out a VCR or DVD at the library. We always have our breath with us wherever we go; so deep breathing is an exceedingly practical and portable technique to help us slow down. *Slowing down provides a way of escape in mania.*

TAKING MANIA SERIOUSLY

Slowing down provides a way of escape in mania. Taking a long-term perspective will help you realize that once the fun and high energy of mania are over, you can be left with pieces to pick up and perhaps a deeper and longer lasting depression. Releasing the gas pedal a bit can make your ride smoother. Recovery skills for mania range from breathing deeply to walking slowly, from taking frequent breaks to pacing with others. Walking away is also an option. All of these tools work because they help you go *beyond bipolar* by slowing down in mania. *Slowing down provides a way of escape in mania.*

Here are some questions to help you look at the idea of slowing down in mania:

1. Is it hard for you to gain long-term perspective? Can you draw a time line of your life or of the past year with bipolar disorder and recognize times of mania and depression? Can you also recognize the impact of mania on your life?

2. Do you know the difference between irritability and anger? Describe times in your life when irritability took over. What effects has irritability had on present and past relationships? Can you identify three or four mood clues for irritability? (You may want to think of a time when you had a temper tantrum or rage and work backward to remember some of the feelings or actions that preceded these events.) Examples of mood clues include sensitivity to sound and light, sharpness in your voice and frustration with minor changes of routine.

3. Contrast how difficult it is to slow down when mania is full blown and when it is just beginning. Can you remember a time when you slowed down instead of fueling mania? How about a time when you encouraged mania to the state of becoming exhausted? Which felt better in the long run? Which occasion had the worst consequences?

4. Part of the illness of bipolar disorder is that we don't always remember how we felt with mania or even what we did. Would it be helpful for you to discuss this with others who have observed your behavior? Choose someone who will be honest and non-judgmental. Can your therapist help you with this?

5. Whether or not you are experiencing mania or hypomania at this time, can you develop a habit of stopping throughout the day to slow yourself down with deep breathing, a short walk or just a moment to soothe your mind? If you are not experiencing mania, can you think about the speed at which your brain is working? Can you watch for those times when it starts working more quickly and see your "brain speed" as a possible mood clue?

6. List some ways to slow down in mania. Can you think of other ways beside those listed in this chapter? Once you have made a list, choose two or three that you think will work for you. Try them out the next time mania gets in the driver's seat and later on reflect on what worked and what didn't.

Conclusion

*Recovery is the process of seeking mental wellness
in the context of experiencing the challenges of bipolar disorder.*

THE INTRODUCTION TO THIS BOOK began with a definition of recovery. It said that *recovery is the process of seeking mental wellness in the context of experiencing the challenges of bipolar disorder.* A key foundational principle to recovery is that it is a process. As a process, it doesn't happen over night or by magic. It takes time and directed activity to get to wellness.

When I was in practice as a family physician, I learned that many disorders are like this. People with any kind of chronic illness did best when they planned to be well and took steps toward wellness. They were motivated by hope and a desire to live a functional life.

Bipolar disorder differs from many chronic illnesses in that it can steal our hope and take away our desire for functioning in major areas of life. It can skew our vision so we are unaware of its grasp on our past, present and future.

When I write about recovery, I see my past and am reminded

of how it seemed I would never get better. I remember the days, months and years of frustration when I lacked the hope of mastering this illness. I also observe my present circumstances and realize that I am potentially vulnerable to future recurrences. I have my bad days, weeks, and occasionally a bad month. However, I can place my progress next to the reality of this illness, and know that the hard work of getting well is worth the energy I have invested in the process.

A long journey has brought me where I am, and much of it was not pretty or safe. There are rocks on the path to wellness—even boulders. I have hiked in the mountains of Colorado where I live. Once, eyes tensely focused downward, I was vigilantly following a difficult and narrow path next to a mountain stream, which was a constant landmark for my journey. When I noticed my hiking partner had chosen to climb onto the boulders that flanked the stream. I called to him and tried to convince him that the path by the stream might be safer and quicker.

Jack continued on the boulder field and called me to join him. When I did, he showed me how to move gracefully from boulder to boulder, using my weight to propel myself forward. He taught me to examine each boulder to choose a path leading to the destination I had chosen. At first, I considered returning to the path by the stream, but soon I gained confidence and learned that I could make quicker progress on the boulders.

Bipolar disorder may seem like a stream whose neighboring path is narrow and challenging. You may be struggling along its path thinking that boulders are impassible, but with training, skill and the help of others who have gone before, you can leave the path by the stream and hike the boulders.

Beyond Bipolar — 7 Steps to Wellness is not a book to read so you can get well. Rather it is a book that challenges you to envision a life of wellness. My goal is that the very least you take from it is the hope and desire to lead a fulfilling life. At the very most, my goal is that you will begin or continue a journey that takes you to wellness and that you enjoy the lights of its city even before you are able to enter it.

Fear can often accompany the setting of high goals. One of my fears is that you will not search for the hope you need to begin the journey, or that, having set out, you will stop to rest and not reach the destination of wellness. Another is that you will expect too much progress too quickly and will give up on the journey.

Stretching for our dreams dissolves fears. My dream for you is that you leave the trail by the stream of bipolar disorder and climb upon the boulders and learn to hike them. The stream may always be present, but from the boulders you can see panoramas beyond the narrow path you have been hiking. With practice, you will find the rhythm of boulder hiking and begin to enjoy a life of wellness *beyond bipolar*.

Excerpt from BeyondBipolar Newsletter

*Psych meds are a lot like a large
extended family that you are marrying into.*

Medications are a challenge for nearly all who have bipolar disorder. Whether you are new to bipolar disorder or an old pro, you may sometimes wonder whether you want medications to become your lifetime pals. Often family members, friends or employers weigh in for or against. Some want you to feel better but don't appreciate that getting better is only the first challenge of bipolar disorder. Staying better is a process that nearly always requires you make medications your friends.

Psych meds are a lot like a large extended family that you are marrying into. You will want to get to know them one or two at a time rather than attending the family reunion and meeting hundreds of cousins at once. You may warm up to part of the family right away, but there may be cousins whom you consider to be black sheep.

If you've ever met the family all at once you may find it impossible to keep in your head who's who. The same is true with the large family of medications that are prescribed for psychiatric and other diagnoses. The doctors, nurse practitioners and physicians assistants who prescribe medicine keep track of medicines by thinking about classes of medications — just as you might keep track of the cousins by remembering which uncle or aunt they belong to.

For instance, there are several classes of medications that are used primarily for high blood pressure. Each class is a part of the family of medicines for high blood pressure, but each part of the family or class works in a different way.

PATIENCE WITH THE COUSINS

One major way in which most medications differ from psychiatric medications is that non-psychiatric medications in a class or family will work pretty much the same for anyone with the condition being treated. For example, there is a class called ACE inhibitors that is used to treat high blood pressure. If your doctor decides that an ACE inhibitor is the class of medication to treat your high blood pressure, it doesn't matter which member of the ACE inhibitor family is chosen. They normally work about the same for each patient. These cousins are agreeable with everyone.

Perhaps with psych meds our brains are a bit pickier. A medication can be chosen from a class or family, but it might not work as well for one person as for the next. So there are many cousins, children of the same aunt and uncle, but they don't perform the same at all. Medications within a class or family will work differently in different people. These cousins don't agree with everyone.

So do doctors still think of classes of medications when prescribing psych meds? Yes, they do! Does it matter which medication within a class is chosen for an individual? Yes, it does! The challenge is, that at this time in our medical knowledge, it is impossible to tell right off the bat which medication will work for whom.

Perhaps this sounds familiar to you. Have you tried one medicine to find that it doesn't work well for you, requiring a switch to a different medicine in the same class or family? The medicines are cousins but they don't look alike. This necessitates patience and some trial and error in finding the medication that will work for you.

Once the medication that works for you is found — you've hit pay dirt and are well on your way to mental wellness. Eureka! Oh, would that it were that simple! Usually it takes multiple trials of medications. Some of us give up too soon and lose the opportunity of finding the medication or combination of medications that will work the best. No pay dirt! No Eureka! More pain, more depression, more mania or hypomania, and more parts of our lives to put back together. We've been through this Humpty-Dumpty thing too many times to give up.

Even when it's hard and takes a long time, persistence can pay off with an excellent chance of achieving mental wellness. Work with your prescriber and give treatment a chance to work for you. Psychiatric disorders are more successfully treated than heart and lung diseases and most forms of cancer.

LONGER TO WORK

Another important key to recognize about psych meds is that most of them take longer to work than do other classes of medications. You take something for high blood pressure or a common infection and the goal is usually accomplished in a few days to a couple of weeks.

The cousins in the psych med branch of the family don't work that way. Psych meds almost always take longer to work than the medications most of us are familiar with. Not understanding the delay between starting a medication and its taking effect can lead to stopping the medication before it has had a chance to work. It may take four to six weeks and sometimes even up to three months for a medication to kick in at its best!

Here's where the art and science of medicine are equally important. Another call for patience as well. Fortunately you may feel better sooner, but it's also easy to give up before you see your medication doing its best work. If only patience could be dolled out generously at the family reunion!

Even More Patience!

Side effects often precede the benefits of many psych meds. Many side effects are uncomfortable and a very few need to be reported right away. Be sure to ask your doctor about which side effects to report right away and which ones you can be patient with. Nearly all side effects will require patience rather than action.

But the patience with side effects has an up side. Many — if not most — side effects will go away after you have been on the medication for a while. Patience with side effects pays off faster than you might expect, sometimes within a week or two.

The nervous system of our body has two parts called the sympathetic and the parasympathetic nervous systems. The sympathetic nervous system kicks in for the so-called flight, fight or freeze response. The parasympathetic system kicks in for every day things like digestion, normal bodily functions and even sex.

Many of the side effects of psych medications affect the parasympathetic system. This means that symptoms such as dry mouth, nausea, constipation and diarrhea can be common. Sexual performance can also be affected.

Side effects can be temporary, so give your parasympathetic system a chance to bounce back. But if side effects continue to bother you, talk to your doctor about ways to manage. In some cases the medication will need to be changed. But these cousins in the family of medications may be ones you can live with after all. And you needn't keep family secrets when side effects arise.

FAMILY SECRETS

Don't keep family secrets about the psychiatric medications you are taking. Instead, write down your concerns and take them with you to your next appointment. You doctor or prescriber should be willing to work with you in a supportive way while you try medications. Your overall goal is to feel better and stay well for as long as possible.

It's challenging to have patience to find the right medication mix, to allow time for new medications to work and to see whether side effects will diminish or resolve. Understanding the family secrets of psych meds can help, but once you learn the family secrets, don't keep them to yourself. Talking to your doctor and to others who have been through the experience of finding the best mix of medications can also boost your morale and help you have patience.

Family members and friends, you be patient too. Taking psych medications is not like popping an aspirin for a headache. Don't expect instant results. Be supportive of your loved one during the process of figuring out the best mix of medications, psychotherapy and recovery skills.

Have appropriate expectations of the process of finding mental wellness in the context of bipolar disorder. There is every reason to have hope, but you may need a good dose of patience before you see your hopes fulfilled. When you marry into a family it takes time to meet the cousins and size them up. The same is true with medications. With patience you may want to be pals with your meds because you feel so much better.

If you would like to receive Dr. Mountain's e-Newsletter, *BeyondBipolar*, sign up now by going to www.BeyondBipolar.com. Find more articles, links, and recommended reading as well.

Glossary

Glossary

Accommodation — Modifications of job duties or a worksite to make it possible for a person with a disability to perform the essential functions of a job. A process of accommodation could involve breaking down a job description into essential and non-essential duties. Non-essential duties could then be assigned to another employee in order to accommodate an employee with a disability. A worksite could be modified to provide a quiet work area for a person who has difficulty concentrating but is able to perform the essential functions of a job. Accommodations are required by law in certain settings. *(See Americans with Disabilities Act and Rehabilitation Act.)*

Activity, goal-directed or purpose-driven — An activity that is carried out with single mindedness and lack of interruption. This type of activity is a characteristic of hypomania.

Americans With Disabilities Act (ADA) — A federal law that prohibits discrimination against people with physical or mental disabilities in employment, public services and places of public accommodation. Bipolar disorder is a covered condition under the ADA. In the worksite, employers have to have more than 15 employees to be required to meet ADA standards.

Bipolar disorder — A mood disorder in which the brain does not consistently regulate mood within a normal range. Bipolar disorder includes a spectrum of disorders, including Bipolar I disorder, Bipolar II disorder and Cyclothymic disorder.

Bipolar disorder, Type I — A bipolar disorder whose chief characteristic is mania punctuated by depression.

Bipolar disorder, Type II — A bipolar disorder whose chief characteristic is depression punctuated by hypomania.

Disability — The condition of having a physical or mental impairment that substantially limits one or more major life activity. Under the Americans with Disabilities act, a person who has a record of such an impairment or is regarded as having such an impairment is protected.

Disclosure — The act of telling facts to others about oneself or one's personal condition. In the context of bipolar disorder, disclosure is telling others of your diagnosis, experience of illness or disability resulting from the illness.

Downtime — Time taken away from normal activities with the purpose of taking care of oneself by actively addressing issues of illness and ways to feel better.

Episode — Episodes of bipolar disorder are defined as discrete periods of illness during which specific features are present as described in the Diagnostic and Statistical Manual, IV-TR (DSM-IV-TR). Major depressive, manic, mixed and hypomanic episodes are described. Technically, they require a threshold number of symptoms lasting for a minimum amount of time, or a hospitalization in the case of mania.

Hope carrier — A person who maintains hope for another when that person is feeling hopeless.

Hypomania — An episode of mood that is in a range above that of normal mood but that is not as extreme as mania. From words meaning "under" and "mania".

Illness experience — The experience a person or family has when having a psychiatric or medical condition. The illness experience is unique to that person or family but contains common elements of others with the illness such as symptoms. An illness experience is different from a medical description of a disorder because it includes day to day challenges, cultural perspectives and individual reactions to the disorder.

Irritability — The condition of responding to annoyance in a way that is increased from normal. In bipolar disorder, irritability results in a low toleration for frustration. Irritability is different from anger in that it is diffusely directed at multiple annoyances rather than at a particular target.

Mania — An episode of mood that is characterized by instability and that is above the range of normal mood.

Manic-depressive disorder — Another term used for bipolar disorder.

Mental wellness — "Mental health refers to the successful performance of mental function, resulting in productive activities, fulfilling relationships with other people, and the ability to adapt to change and cope with adversity." (*Mental Health: A Report of the Surgeon General*, 1999, p. 4)

Mixed Mood — An episode of mood outside the range of normal that includes characteristics of depression and mania/hypomania occurring at the same time.

Mood chart — A charting tool used to graph mood in order to help observe changes in mood. Mood charts are also called mood graphs and mood diaries.

Normal mood — Mood that is regulated by the brain to stay within a normal range. Normal mood varies and includes sadness and elation but underlying normal mood is a feeling of contentment of happiness most of the time. Normal mood is resilient within the range of normal.

Obsessive-compulsive disorder — A disorder characterized by compulsions or obsessions taking up considerable time and recognized as excessive or unreasonable.

Psychomotor retardation — A condition often associated with depression, in which decreased physical activity is associated with a slowing of mental activity.

Psychotherapy — Treatment whose goal is improved mental health. In the context of bipolar disorder, many effective psychotherapy treatments have been developed which result in fewer hospitalizations and extremes of mood. Psychotherapy is sometimes called "talk therapy". From two words meaning "mind" and "treatment".

Racing thoughts — Rapid thinking associated with mania or hypomania. Often the person experiencing racing thoughts will not perceive them as such, but will have the sensation that the world has slowed or that thoughts are intrusive, interfering with concentration and focus.

Rapid cycling — Technically, rapid cycling is diagnosed when there are four or more distinct episodes of depression, mania or hypomania within one year. However, the episodes are likely to be more frequent than four times yearly.

Recovery group — A group of peers (those sharing a common experience) who meet regularly with their primary purpose to support one another, learn recovery skills, and seek wellness.

Rehabilitation Act — a body of federal legislation that protects the rights of individuals from discrimination on the basis of disability. It applies to federal agencies, program receiving federal monies, federal employment and the employment practices of federal contractors.

Resilience — The ability to bounce back when faced with adversity. In this book resilience also applies to the ability to help one's moods become resilient in or near the range of normal mood.

Sentinel mood clue — Early mood clues are appear consistently and that signify that mood is changing or has changed from one mood state to another.

Street Knowledge — The knowledge we get from others who live with bipolar disorder on a day to day basis and have found ways to become resilient.

Support group — A group of peers facing similar conditions who listen to each other and provide encouragement in mutual challenges. (See also recovery groups.)

Switching — A change in mood state, usually associated with rapidity.

Index

italic = definition
bold = main discussion

A

Need a speaker?

J ANE MOUNTAIN, MD, IS A SPEAKER as well as an author. She brings passion and professionalism to the topic of recovery from bipolar disorder and other mental health topics. Your audiences will leave with take-home messages that they can begin using right away.

Here's what one client said about Dr. Mountain's Keynote address:

> We have received nothing but positive feedback about Dr. Mountain's presentation.... She provides an excellent combination of structured information and personal stories, which serve to make the topic real. Our audience had a wide variation of knowledge, ranging from therapists and physicians to individuals coping with the loss of a loved one to suicide. No matter what the level of prior knowledge, audience members responded positively to Dr. Mountain's presentation, and walked away with a more in depth understanding.... *Executive Director Suicide Resource Center of Larimer County (Colorado)*

Dr. Mountain provides Keynotes, Training, and Inservices to a variety of audiences. Your audiences will be delighted and leave with hope and clarity.

Learn more at www.BeyondBipolar.com.

Beyond Bipolar —
7 Steps to Wellness

*Hope is the essential ingredient
of the recovery process.*

Management drives resiliency.

*Resiliency is the target we aim for
to achieve mental wellness.*

*Discovering mood clues is essential
in playing the game of bipolar disorder.*

*Depression and mania
are linked through
mood regulation.*

*Activation provides an escape
from depression.*

*Slowing down provides an escape
from mania.*